ROOTED *in* HEALTH

ROOTED
in
HEALTH

The Bastyr University Story

KATHLEEN O'CONNOR

CHRISTINE UMMEL HOSLER

OUR MISSION

We educate future leaders in the
natural health arts and sciences.
Respecting the healing power of nature
and recognizing that body, mind,
and spirit are intrinsically inseparable,
we model an integrated approach
to education, research
and clinical service.

Dedicated to those whose conviction,
vision, and commitment realized the dream
that the natural health arts and sciences will
truly transform health care and the health
of the human community.

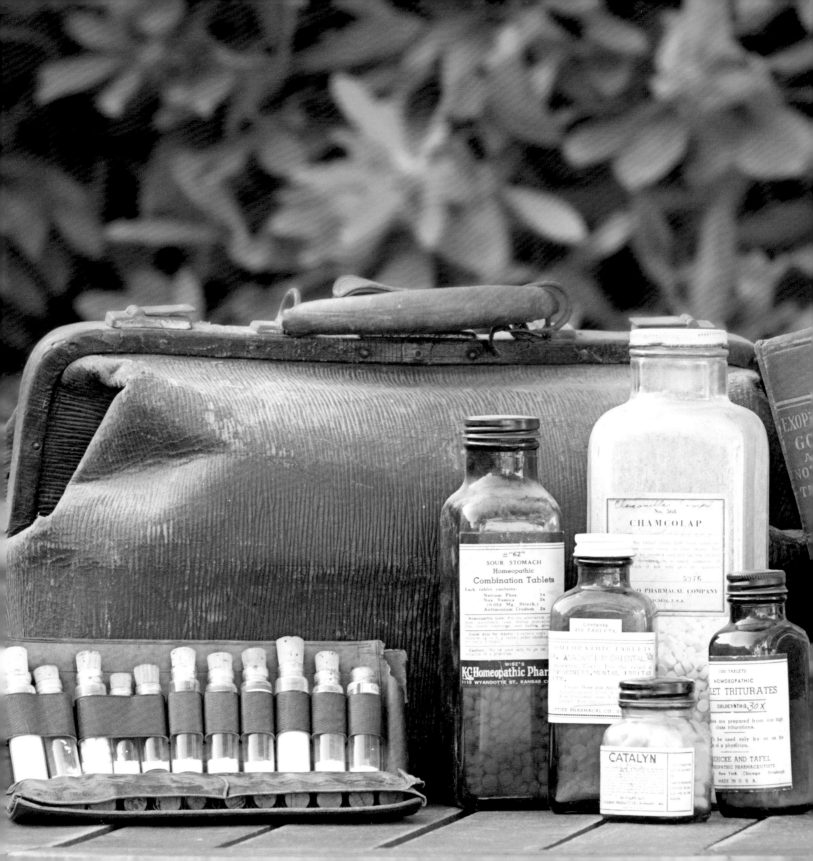

CONTENTS

FOREWORD
13

Left: *Dr. John Bastyr's medical bag and natural remedies*

FOREWORD

What began as a movement fewer than two score years ago has become an institution. Not everyone thinks that is a good thing.

What has become Bastyr University, the world's leading academic center for the advancement and integration of knowledge in the natural health arts and sciences, was born of a passion to save a dying profession and secure a place in the future for the medicine in which the founders so fervently believed. Perhaps these amazing pioneers knew relatively little about establishing an academic institution, but they knew everything they needed to know about how to articulate and promulgate the principles of naturopathic medicine they had been taught and the practice of which they feared was in jeopardy

In this little book, envisioned in 2012 during the centennial of the birth of John Bartholomew Bastyr, the authors have put together a brief narrative that captures the energy of the movement as it gathered momentum and evolved into the multidisciplinary university the founders might never have envisioned. Some people have described the process as a loss of purpose as the organization moved away from a singular focus on naturopathic medicine to an embrace of some twenty degree programs at the baccalaureate, master's, and doctoral levels. Others celebrate the maturation of the field and the recognition that a shared philosophy underlies all that Bastyr University teaches.

The brevity of this account belies its significance. There are few examples of such a marvelous success story in the larger world. Imagine moving so quickly from $200 of start-up funds to an annual operating budget nearing $50 million. Imagine the shift from teaching in a rented classroom at a local community college to operating two flourishing campuses and two respected teaching clinics.

This is our story.

—Daniel K. Church, PhD
President, 2005-2015

Left: Echinacea purpurea, *purple coneflower*

BASTYR UNIVERSITY
TIMELINE

1978
- The offices of the John Bastyr College of Naturopathic Medicine (JBCNM) open on July 1.
- Orientation for the inaugural class takes place on September 21.

1980
- First teaching clinic opens. Quarter-time librarian hired.

1982
- JBCNM graduates the first class of ND students from a Washington state college of naturopathic medicine in more than twenty years.
- College hires a part-time academic dean for basic sciences and a half-time dean of students.
- Certificate in Naturopathic Midwifery is established.
- College moves into leased space at surplused F. A. McDonald Elementary School.

1983
- JBCNM becomes the first college of naturopathic medicine to be recognized as a candidate for accreditation by the Northwest Association of Schools and Colleges (NASC).

1984
- Bachelor of Science and Master of Science in Nutrition programs are established.
- Name of school is changed to John Bastyr College. Teaching clinic is renamed Bastyr College of Natural Medicine Clinic.

1985
- *A Textbook of Natural Medicine*, authored by Bastyr College President Joseph Pizzorno Jr. and Michael T. Murray, ND ('85), is published.

1986
- Bastyr Research Center opens.

1987
- Doctor of Naturopathic Medicine program is accredited by the Council on Naturopathic Medical Education (CNME).
- Washington state legislature passes the Naturopathic Practices Act (RCW 18.36A), broadening naturopathic physicians' scope of practice.

1989
- Master of Science in Acupuncture and Oriental Medicine is established.
- Bastyr College is granted accreditation by NASC, retroactive to September 1988.

1990

- Bastyr College's teaching clinic relocates to Seattle's Wallingford District.
- The Bastyr Research Center completes the Healing AIDS Research Project, a pilot study of the effects of alternative treatments on a small group of patients with AIDS symptoms.

1992

- Bastyr College partners with the Leadership Institute of Seattle (LIOS) to offer courses in counseling and behavioral sciences.

1993

- Didactic Program in Dietetics is approved by the American Dietetic Association.
- Washington State Insurance Commissioner Deborah Senn invites Bastyr College to help create models for better inclusion of complementary medicine in the state health care plan.

1994

- School name is changed to Bastyr University to acknowledge expansion into a multidisciplinary institution. The teaching clinic is renamed Bastyr University Natural Health Clinic.
- Accreditation status is granted by the National Commission for Schools and Colleges of Acupuncture and Oriental Medicine.
- The National Institutes of Health (NIH) Office of Alternative Medicine awards Bastyr an $840,000, three-year grant to study how people with AIDS respond to complementary and alternative medical treatments.
- "Sister-school" agreement is established with Chengdu University of Traditional Medicine in China.
- Certificate in Chinese Herbal Medicine program is established.

1995

- University receives Ryan White federal funds, enabling the teaching clinic to provide free natural health care to low-income patients living with HIV/AIDS.
- Death of John Bartholomew Bastyr, DC, ND, renowned Seattle physician after whom Bastyr University is named.

1996

- Bastyr is awarded contract to locate and run King County Natural Medicine Clinic, the nation's first government-run natural medicine clinic.
- University relocates to 51-acre campus in Kenmore, Washington.

1997

- Bastyr University Cancer Research Center is founded.

1998

- Bachelor of Science with a Major in Health Psychology is established.
- Bastyr students organize the first Haunted Trails fundraising event, which will become a Halloween tradition.

1999

- Jane Guiltinan, ND ('86), dean of clinical affairs, is appointed to the board of Harborview Medical Center, becoming the first ND to serve on a public hospital board in the United States.
- Bastyr holds its first annual Herb and Food Fair.

2000

- Bachelor of Science with a Major in Exercise Science and Wellness established.
- Thomas T. and Elizabeth C. Tierney Basic Sciences Research Laboratory opens, becoming the first research laboratory established at a natural health arts and sciences university.
- Bastyr University Natural Health Clinic changes name to Bastyr Center for Natural Health to reflect breadth of services offered.
- Thomas Shepherd, DHA, becomes the second president of Bastyr University.

2001

- Bachelor of Science with a Major in Herbal Sciences is established.
- Bastyr establishes "sister-school" agreement with Shanghai University of Traditional Medicine in China.
- Bastyr begins using "earth tubs" to compost the University's food waste for use in the medicinal herb garden.

2002

- University receives its first million-dollar gift from an individual, Stephen Bing of Los Angeles. The funds are used to build a state-of-the-art whole-food teaching kitchen.
- Naturopathic medicine residency program at Bastyr Center for Natural Health is certified by Council on Naturopathic Medical Education (CNME).
- Bastyr hosts the first annual "CAM Camp," which introduces University of Washington School of Nursing faculty to the basics of complementary and alternative medicine (CAM).
- Bastyr is awarded a five-year collaborative grant from the National Center for Complementary and Alternative Medicine (NCCAM), part of the National Institutes of Health, to prepare scientists to conduct CAM research.
- With Bastyr's leadership, the American Association of Naturopathic Medical Colleges (AANMC) is established.

2003

- Doctor of Acupuncture and Oriental Medicine (DAOM) program established.

2004

- Master of Science in Nutrition and Clinical Health Psychology established.
- Reflexology Foot Path is built by Bastyr volunteers, becoming the first public path of its kind in the nation.
- Bastyr University Press publishes a cookbook, *From the Bastyr Kitchen*.

2005

- Daniel K. Church, PhD, becomes the third president of Bastyr.
- Bastyr purchases its 51-acre Kenmore campus from the Catholic Archdiocese of Seattle.

2006

- Bastyr partners with HerbDay Coalition, celebrates first annual national HerbDay.
- Bastyr Center relocates to an expanded facility in Seattle's Wallingford neighborhood.

2007

- University receives $2 million anonymous donation, the largest in the school's history to date.
- DAOM program receives professional accreditation, making Bastyr the first academic institution in the United States with a both regionally and professionally accredited DAOM program.
- Co-founder William A. Mitchell, Jr., ND, passes away at age 59.
- First-ever conference on "The State of Science of Botanical Authentication" is held at Bastyr.
- Transportation initiative begins to reduce the University's environmental footprint.

2008

- Bastyr Center for Natural Health receives LEED certification by the U.S. Green Building Council for sustainable building materials and practices.
- The National Wildlife Federation recognizes the University as an exemplary and committed school in its 2008 National Report Card on Sustainability in Higher Education.
- Bastyr University launches a comprehensive, campus-wide composting initiative.
- The Bastyr Integrative Oncology Research Clinic (BIORC) is established.

■ Four Elements Garden is established at the eastern edge of the Medicinal Herb Garden.

■ Founders' Awards established to honor the founders and recognize excellence in faculty, staff, students, and alumni.

2009

■ Bachelor of Science with a Major in Nutrition and Exercise Science is established.

■ Bachelor of Science with a Major in Nutrition and Culinary Arts is established.

2010

■ Bastyr University merges with Seattle Midwifery School and establishes the only direct-entry Master of Science in Midwifery degree in the United States that is both regionally accredited and accredited by the Midwifery Education Accreditation Council (MEAC).

■ Bachelor of Science with a Major in Integrative Human Biology is established.

■ Certificate in Holistic Landscape Design is established.

■ Bastyr opens the Student Village, with housing for 132 students, which later

wins LEED-platinum certification and Outstanding Multifamily Project of the year award from the U.S. Green Building Council.

■ Bastyr University and Fred Hutchinson Cancer Research Center receive $3.1 million NIH grant for integrative breast cancer research.

■ Bastyr receives $4.52 million NIH grant for the Bastyr/UW Oncomycology Translational Research Center to study the healing effects of Asian medicinal mushrooms on breast and prostate cancer.

■ Center for Spirituality, Science and Medicine is established.

■ The first named building on the Kenmore campus is in the Student Village—named by a generous, anonymous alumna in honor of her favorite professor, Dr. Eric Jones.

2011

■ Bastyr Bikes program and electric car-charging stations are introduced to promote green transportation.

■ Center for Health Policy and Leadership is established.

■ Bastyr University becomes a member of United Nations Academic Impact (UNAI).

2012

■ Bastyr University California opens in San Diego, welcoming 49 students to its inaugural Doctor of Naturopathic Medicine class.

■ Bastyr University Clinic opens, becoming the teaching clinic for Bastyr University California while also offering comprehensive health care to the San Diego community.

■ Master of Arts in Counseling Psychology is established.

■ Bastyr University honors the 100th year of the birth of its namesake, Dr. John Bastyr, with a year-long centennial celebration.

2013

■ Master of Science in Ayurvedic Sciences is established, becoming the first such accredited program in North America.

■ School of Traditional World Medicines is created.

■ Bastyr University faculty members help formulate a line of Choice Organic Wellness Teas, from which a portion of the proceeds goes to student scholarships.

■ Bastyr University introduces animal protein into the formerly vegetarian Dining Commons.

2014

■ Center for Social Justice and Diversity created to lead University's work addressing inequality in health care.

2015

■ After ten years of service as Bastyr's third president, Dr. Daniel K. Church retires.

■ Bastyr launches Master of Public Health (MPH), Master of Arts in Maternal-Child Health Systems, and Master of Science in Nutrition for Wellness, signaling the University's growth in community-level wellness.

■ Griffith Hall, Mitchell Hall, Pizzorno Hall, and Quinn Hall are named to honor the founders.

SOIL

As recently as sixty years ago, it appeared that the practice of natural medicine was a dying profession in the United States. Conventionally trained doctors and naturopathic doctors looked on each other as competitors in an irreconcilable conflict—and in that conflict, natural medicine seemed destined to lose.

Science brought the world infection-fighting penicillin and an antibiotic cure for tuberculosis in the 1940s; polio vaccine in 1955; and the first successful human heart transplant in 1967. Conventional medicine, with its mechanistic view of health and disease, was elevated to a new pinnacle of authority as the way of the future. From that position of power, the American Medical Association (AMA) targeted "alternative medicine;" its Committee on Quackery, founded in 1964, labeled chiropractic "an unscientific cult" and actively worked to eliminate it as a profession.

Naturopathic doctors were licensed in about one-third of U.S. states in the 1940s, and numerous four-year naturopathic medical schools existed, but by 1957 only one naturopathic college was left. The last Doctor of Naturopathic Medicine (ND) program in the United States, at the Western States College of Chiropractic, ended in 1956.

Several doctors from that program founded the National College of Naturopathic Medicine in Portland, Oregon, to keep their profession alive. Yet by 1975, only eight states still licensed naturopathic physicians, and the practice of naturopathic medicine was a felony in two states. The most recent textbook on naturopathic medicine, *Naturae Medicina and Naturopathic Dispensatory*, edited by Dr. A. W. Kuts-Cheraux, had been published decades before, in 1953.

Today we live in a very different world. Conventional doctors and naturopathic doctors, formerly rivals and antagonists, are collaborating in partnerships that would have seemed impossible even twenty years ago.

Left: Bellis perennis, *common daisy*

IT'S A FACT

The healing power of nature was recognized more than 2,400 years ago by Hippocrates, a Greek physician who became an iconic figure in the history of medicine.

- The National Center for Complementary and Integrative Health (formerly the National Center for Complementary and Alternative Medicine) at the National Institutes of Health uses its federal appropriation—$123.8 million in fiscal year 2013—to determine, through scientific research, the effectiveness and safety of treatments such as botanical remedies, movement therapy, meditation, and acupuncture.
- The Council on Naturopathic Medical Education, a national accrediting agency recognized by the U.S. Department of Education, has granted accreditation to seven institutions that award ND degrees in the United States.
- According to a 2011 report conducted by the Samueli Institute, 42% of U.S. hospitals offer one or more complementary, alternative, and integrative medicine treatments.
- More than fifty U.S. and Canadian medical schools and teaching hospitals, organized as the Consortium of Academic Health Centers for Integrative Medicine, include CAM in their curriculum.

How did so much radical change happen so quickly? Many factors and cultural forces were at work. One factor was Bastyr University. The school's namesake, Dr. John Bastyr, inspired the new generation of NDs to integrate science and the healing arts in their practice. The University's founders, Drs. Les Griffith, William A. Mitchell, Jr., and Joseph E. Pizzorno Jr., and Sheila Quinn, were instrumental in ensuring the long-term viability of naturopathic medicine and other natural healing disciplines—as were countless others in the Bastyr community who studied, taught, treated, researched, advocated for, and otherwise contributed to the success of the school over the past three and one-half decades.

CHAPTER ONE

SEEDS

Bastyr University is named in honor of the renowned Seattle-area naturopathic physician and teacher who championed science-based natural medicine. Dr. John Bastyr helped generations of Seattle families through a private practice that spanned more than fifty years. Believing it his duty to serve patients regardless of their finances or situation, he charged low fees, kept his office open for extended hours, and frequently made late-night house calls for free.

Often what made the biggest impression on both his patients and his students—in addition to his knowledge, which was considerable—was his way of caring for people. He truly listened to his patients, being fully present to them, and used gentle touch to connect with them. Because they trusted him and were able to open up to him, he was more able to detect the causes of their symptoms.

Dr. Bastyr believed that the patient, not the doctor, does the curing, and he always encouraged his patients to take responsibility for their own health and actively seek wellness, a philosophy that would inform Bastyr University from its beginnings. He integrated therapies from diverse sources based on naturopathic principles of practice, science, and individual patients' needs.

The Life of a Healer

John Bartholomew Bastyr was born in 1912 in New Prague, Minnesota, the son of a pharmacist employed by a drug company. His mother was a devotee of nutrition, gardening, medicinal herbs, and hydrotherapy, and introduced him to the world of natural healing. John's

IT'S A FACT

John Bastyr, ND, whose treatments relied on both nature and science, is widely recognized as having been an influential figure in the resurgence of naturopathic medicine in the United States.

Right, both photos:
Before his death in 1995, Dr. Bastyr was a regular visitor to the medical school bearing his name

Left: *Dr. John Bastyr's healing hands*

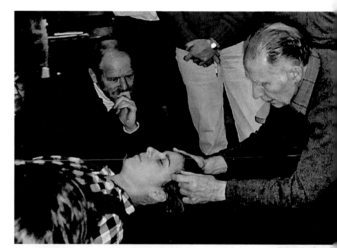

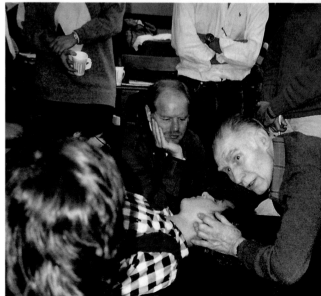

Dr. Bastyr visits with early Bastyr students

appendix was removed when he was nine, and the incision later reopened while he was climbing a tree. His mother applied a poultice of broadleaf plantain to the wound, and it healed neatly and quickly.

In 1928, the family moved to Seattle, where John's father opened a pharmacy. John helped by making deliveries and running the soda fountain. In a 1989 oral-history interview, he recalled watching his father fill prescriptions, sometimes calling medical doctors to warn them they'd ordered potentially lethal combinations of incompatible drugs.

The young man began studying the basics of botanical and homeopathic pharmacy while attending Seattle College High School (now known as Seattle Prep). After graduation, he attended Seattle College of Chiropractic, where he earned his doctor of chiropractic degree

in 1931. Over the next five years, he completed a residency at Grace Hospital and received a naturopathic diploma. Soon after, he opened a private practice in Georgetown.

Dr. Bastyr would continue treating patients into his eighties. A respected midwife, he provided pre- and post-natal care to women and their children, and managed hundreds of home births. Over his remarkable career, many families trusted Dr. Bastyr with the delivery of two generations of children. He received a World War II deferment because he was delivering so many babies, traveling wherever laboring mothers needed him, at all hours of the day and night.

"Some weeks I remember going maybe a week, seven days, without getting horizontal to sleep," he told one interviewer. "Just stand up in a corner and sleep a bit."

Tireless Advocate for Natural Medicine

Throughout his life, Dr. Bastyr lobbied the Washington state legislature for recognition of naturopathic medicine. He also played a key role in establishing the Seattle branch of the National College of Naturopathic Medicine (NCNM), where he would serve as a teacher, board member, and president.

The three naturopathic doctors who founded the John Bastyr College of Naturopathic Medicine in 1978 had all benefited from his teaching and his persuasive advocacy for natural medicine.

Joseph Pizzorno, Jr. was a third-year student at NCNM when negative court decisions threatened to impede the practice of natural medicine. He asked Dr. Bastyr whether naturopathy had a future. "The truth of our medicine will out," his mentor responded, echoing a quote from Shakespeare. "The truth of what we are doing will always survive." In spite of being such an inspiration to the College's founders, Dr. Bastyr initially expressed uneasiness about the school being named for him. A deeply humble man, he tried to avoid having people make a fuss over him or his accomplishments. Later on, however, the founders were deeply pleased when he commented that he would like to have an honorary degree from the University.

Dr. Griffith, Dr. Pizzorno, and Dr. Mitchell, knew they had picked the right man. Dr. Mitchell referred to his teacher as "the father of modern naturopathic thought." Deeply committed to science-based natural medicine, Dr. Bastyr worked tirelessly researching medical literature and applying the latest findings to naturopathic principles. He strove to verify his results with laboratory studies.

Following Dr. Bastyr's death in 1995 at the age of 83, many of his colleagues and students credited him with rescuing the field from obscurity after several decades of declining public interest. As Dr. Mitchell put it, "The continuance of naturopathic medicine as a viable healing art rested solely on the shoulders of a very few people, and John Bastyr was one of those people."

Below: *A bust of the school's namesake is unveiled on the campus with Dr. William Mitchell, Dr. John Bastyr, Dr. Joseph Pizzorno, and Earl Darley, the artist*

CHAPTER TWO

ROOTS

The future looked bleak for natural medicine in Washington in 1978. The Seattle campus of the National College of Naturopathic Medicine (NCNM) had closed two years earlier. With no new graduates signing up to take the licensing examinations, Washington state legislators planned to eliminate naturopathic licensing.

Three recent NCNM graduates decided they couldn't let that happen. Les Griffith, who had graduated from Western Washington University with a master's degree in psychology, had brought his Everett neighbor, William A. Mitchell, Jr., along on his first visit to check out NCNM. Mitchell had studied at Marquette University, then transferred to the University of Washington, graduating with a bachelor's degree in history. He paid his way through naturopathic college by giving guitar lessons.

Joseph E. Pizzorno, Jr. had come to naturopathic medicine after graduating in chemistry from Harvey Mudd College, intending to become a medical researcher. Following his graduation from NCNM, he started his own private practice; when Dr. Mitchell graduated a year later, Dr. Pizzorno invited him to join his practice.

Around Dr. Mitchell's kitchen table one evening in April of 1978, the three friends agreed to start a new naturopathic college in Seattle. Not only would its existence persuade the state to continue licensing naturopathic doctors, but the right school might help trigger a resurgence of interest in natural medicine.

A New Vision

We dreamed of what the perfect naturopathic institution would look like—what it would need, what its focus would be," said Dr.

Left: Each spring, new plants take root as nature's growing cycle begins anew in the Bastyr University Gardens, Kenmore

IT'S A FACT

Start-up budget for the school that would become Bastyr University: $200

Griffith. "We had already decided on the basic foundation—science-based and accredited." When Dr. Pizzorno articulated their vision for the school while recruiting faculty, students, and board members, he coined the term "science-based natural medicine" to describe what the founders wanted to accomplish.

The founders believed that curriculum had to be based on science. They wanted proof that natural treatments and therapies were effective in preventing and treating diseases. Naturopathic doctors (NDs) needed to learn to speak the same language as their medical and scientific counterparts. Otherwise, their work would never be taken seriously by the wider medical establishment.

Not everyone embraced this vision. At the time, naturopathic medicine generally was based on anecdotal observation and patient reports. NDs were taught by practitioners who passed along a compendium of healing traditions practiced for centuries. Many naturopathic doctors saw Dr. Bastyr's new scientific approach as a betrayal of the natural healing arts, an attempt to force them into the conventional, allopathic model of medicine and, eventually, reliance on pharmaceutical drugs and surgery.

Despite this, Drs. Griffith, Pizzorno, and Mitchell were undeterred. Later that year they founded the new school, naming it the John Bastyr College of Naturopathic Medicine (JBCNM).

One of their first decisions—and one of their smartest, they said—was hiring Sheila Quinn. Mavis Bonnar, then married to Dr. Pizzorno, worked with Quinn at the University of Washington School of Medicine and recommended her as an experienced medical school administrator. Once Quinn grasped what the three naturopathic physicians hoped to accomplish, she joined the team, giving up a secure job with a regular salary, a retirement plan, and benefits, to become the fourth founder of this uncertain venture.

THE FOUNDERS

William A. Mitchell, Jr., ND

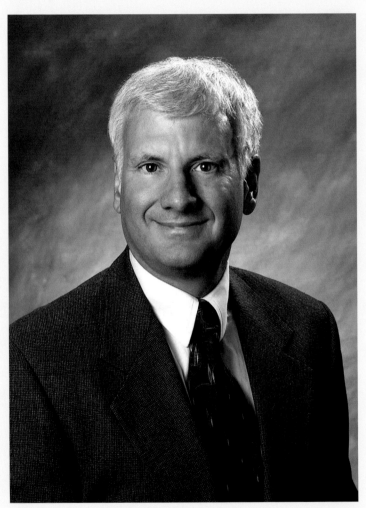

Joseph E. Pizzorno, Jr., ND

Lester Griffith, ND

Sheila Quinn

The four quickly settled on their respective roles. Dr. Griffith would focus on legislative and regulatory issues, of which there were many. Dr. Mitchell would become director of admissions. Quinn, the only paid employee, would build an administrative structure and a bare-bones five-year plan. Dr. Pizzorno would serve as JBCNM's first president.

Their starting budget? A gift of $200, from one of Dr. Pizzorno's grateful patients, who was also the mother of his receptionist. Giving him the check, she told him, "I want there to be more doctors like you!"

A Rough First Year

When asked later how JBCNM survived its first few years, Dr. Griffith explained that "the belief was so strong it overcame all the obstacles."

Many obstacles stood in the way of the creation of a modern naturopathic medical school. No pool of qualified students existed. The most modern textbook on naturopathic medicine was twenty-five years old, and there was no scientific journal for the profession. Media coverage of anything involving natural healing was always negative. JBCNM had no financial backing, and no foundations would provide financial support. When the College's office opened on July 1, 1978, Quinn's modest paycheck was coming out of $35 application fees and $200 enrollment deposits.

Yet the right support kept appearing at the right time. Classroom space became available through one of Dr. Pizzorno's connections. Because of his undergraduate work in chemistry, he had acquaintances among the basic sciences faculty at Seattle Central Community College (SCCC). Dr. Pizzorno knew the dean of sciences, whose favorite uncle was a naturopathic doctor in California; the dean was willing to develop a program with JBCNM.

The resulting partnership yielded both classroom and laboratory space as well as a few instructors. JBCNM contracted with some of the SCCC faculty to teach basic science courses in the core curriculum for the first two years. This bought time for Dr. Pizzorno and Jeff Bland, PhD, the first member of the school's Board of Trustees, to develop the clinical curriculum they would need in

Right: *Early classes of students met in a surplused elementary school in Seattle*

years three and four. They used the curriculum from the National College of Naturopathic Medicine as a starting point.

The arrangement with SCCC also helped JBCNM obtain approval from the Washington State Council on Postsecondary Education to operate as an institution of higher education. The founders used their initial $200 to print student-recruitment brochures, which they mailed to naturopathic doctors' offices. News of JBCNM spread quickly by word of mouth. Thirty-one students enrolled to attend classes starting in September 1978.

Then, suddenly, the new College's luck seemed to run out. The University of Washington School of Medicine learned that a naturopathic medical school was becoming affiliated with SCCC, and it took legal action. The university and other critics of natural medicine successfully lobbied the chancellor of the state's community college system to prevent JBCNM students from being taught by community college faculty members, whose salaries were subsidized by Washington's taxpayers. The school faced possible closure a week before classes were to begin in late September.

Dr. Pizzorno quickly appealed the decision to the chancellor of the Seattle Community Colleges District. The chancellor was sympathetic to JBCNM's cause, and he and the school worked out a solution. ND students could take basic science classes from the community college faculty, under a new contract between JBCNM and SCCC, which required that ND students enroll in—and pay tuition at—both institutions.

The downside was that JBCNM students suddenly faced paying much higher quarterly tuition. Under the original plan, ND students would have paid approximately $300 per quarter to JBCNM and $275 per quarter to SCCC. The tuition to JBCNM now increased to $700 a quarter. JBCNM had to cover the cost of contracting instructors through SCCC, as well as renting classrooms, a lab, and a lecture hall.

Some students had already sold their homes or businesses to pay for their educations. Financial aid was available for Seattle Central classes but not, at first, for JBCNM classes. Yet not a single student walked away from his or her commitment to attend. Despite the obstacles, the John Bastyr College of Naturopathic Medicine started classes on time, with a small but remarkable group of dedicated students.

CHAPTER THREE

FIRST BUDS

Orientation for the inaugural class took place on September 21, 1978. Everything belonging to JBCNM—a small library, records, admissions files—had to fit into a single room, a converted broom closet on the SCCC campus. So did the desks used by Sheila Quinn as the school's administrator and Dr. Pizzorno as the president. Because of the very limited space and budget, Dr. Pizzorno made bookshelves to fit above the desks from plywood he cut and stained in his garage.

Most non-SCCC faculty members taught their first classes without pay. "We would talk to people who had skills we needed and somehow talk them into coming on board, almost always with no money . . . with the promise of 'Someday it'll get better, and when it gets better, we'll pay you,'" said Dr. Griffith. "Even those who got some pay, it was never a real salary."

Hands-on Training

After two years of basic science courses, JBCNM's first class was ready to start clinical training in fall of 1980. JBCNM needed a clinic where patients could be examined, diagnosed, and treated. SCCC could not provide such space, so a suitable facility was found on the second floor of a bank building at 45th Street and University Way, near the University of Washington campus. The new John Bastyr College of Naturopathic Medicine Clinic had room for patient visits, a laboratory, and a pharmacy, as well as administrative staff.

JBCNM recruited practicing naturopathic doctors as instructors. Early faculty members came mostly

Left: Prunus sp, *cherry blossom*

IT'S A FACT

Number of Bastyr graduates in 1981-82: 31

Right: *Students gather at the surplused McDonald Elementary School in Seattle's Wallingford neighborhood in the early 1980s*

from the greater Seattle area, though some traveled from Oregon and British Columbia—often on weekends and at their own expense. Some local clinical faculty members brought their own patients to the University District facility on days when they were teaching. This gave students the opportunity to examine and diagnose patients and to make treatment recommendations under the supervision of practicing naturopathic doctors.

However, the biggest source of patients was Dr. Pizzorno's practice. During the first two years of JBCNM's existence, Dr. Pizzorno still practiced naturopathic medicine half-time. When the clinic opened, Dr. Pizzorno

*Students work together
in lab classes*

brought his whole practice to the teaching clinic so students would have patients on the first day.

Downstairs from the clinic, a single room with a separate entrance was converted to a cadaver lab, where students could learn the intricacies of the human body. This ground floor space was used exclusively for anatomy classes and dissections. Representatives from JBCNM went to hospital auctions and acquired surgical tables that were going cheap or being discarded; those became the cadaver tables for anatomy classes.

With some difficulty, JBCNM arranged for the UW's Anatomy Department to supply cadavers. However, the only way they could be discreetly delivered was for drivers to come up the alley behind the clinic late at night and lift the corpses through the back windows.

Collections and Collaborations

No post-graduate institution can thrive without a library. JBCNM's began as a hastily gathered collection of books donated by retired naturopathic physicians and other friends of the college. Susan Gloriod, a first-year student with a master's degree in library science, organized the initial collection of 650 volumes and 50 journal subscriptions.

JBCNM set a goal of growing the library by 200 volumes per year. Students also had access to the SCCC library and to extensive collections at the UW's Health Sciences Library. Deborah Caplow, MLS, was hired as a quarter-time librarian; her role evolved into a full-time position by the 1985–1986 academic year, and she continued to serve at Bastyr until the year 2000.

During the same time, Bastyr co-founder Dr. Pizzorno collaborated with then-student Michael T. Murray, on a reference book about naturopathic medicine. The *Textbook of Natural Medicine* was published in 1985. Now in its fourth edition, it is considered the definitive work on natural medicine for health care professionals worldwide.

Top: *Dr. Pizzorno addresses an early convocation*
Above: *Dr. Mitchell in the dispensary*

LAURELS OF HONOR

Countless faculty, staff, students, alumni, friends and supporters over the past three decades have helped to make Bastyr University what it is today. While we cannot list every contributor, here are a few noteworthy names of staff and faculty who have accomplished significant gains for the University.

Jeffrey Basom
Head Chef, 1987-2012
Established the first campus food service. Author of *From the Bastyr Kitchen*, the first volume published by Bastyr University Press.

Timothy C. Callahan, PhD
1992-
Served in more positions than any other Bastyr University employee—guest lecturer, adjunct faculty member, assistant professor, director of research integrity, director of institutional assessment, dean of undergraduate education, associate vice president for academics, interim vice president for academics and research, vice president for research and collaboration, director of the Bastyr University Research Institute, senior vice president and provost.

Richard Frederickson, PhD
Professor of Pathology, 1986-2014
First faculty member named to emeritus status.

Sheldon Haber
Vice President for Finance and Administration, 1991-
First chief financial officer.

John Hibbs, ND
Clinical Professor of Naturopathic Medicine, 1985-
Longest-serving faculty member.

Eric Jones, ND
Clinical Professor of Naturopathic Medicine, 1989-
First person for whom a campus building was named (through the gift of an anonymous alumna).

Gowsala Sivam, PhD
Professor of Chemistry, 1998-2011
First faculty member to retire from Bastyr University.

Sanford (Sandy) Voit
Dean of Students, 1982-2001
First dean of students; first chair of the Bastyr University Alumni Association.

Susan L. Weider, MA
Vice President for Student Affairs, 2001-
Oversaw the widest continuum of services—marketing, admissions, financial aid, registrar, student services, career services and alumni affairs—to ensure a seamless movement of students from first encounter to lifelong supporter.

Left: *The first class of naturopathic doctors graduates in 1982 at the Saint Thomas Center in Kenmore*

Above: *Signing diplomas for the first commencement*

The First Graduation

The first class of naturopathic doctors (NDs) graduated from JBCNM in 1982 in a ceremony held at a Catholic seminary called Saint Thomas the Apostle in Kenmore, at the north end of Lake Washington. It was the first graduation of ND students from a college of naturopathic medicine in Washington state in more than twenty years. The commencement speech was given by Dr. Joe Boucher, a beloved naturopathic physician who later became the namesake of a naturopathic college in Vancouver, British Columbia.

The same year, JBCNM hired a part-time academic dean for basic sciences, as well as a half-time dean of students, who had a joint appointment with SCCC.

The community college had been essential as an incubator during Bastyr's first years, but it offered no room for expansion. Faculty and administrators needed office space, and there was no place for the growing library. Also, many SCCC students and instructors smoked, creating a less-than-ideal environment for focusing on health.

So JBCNM moved into leased space at the F. A. McDonald Elementary School, a surplused Seattle Public Schools property in the Wallingford/Latona neighborhood. The College's new location had office space, classrooms, meeting rooms, even an outdoor area suitable for a small herb garden. Now Bastyr had room to grow.

THE BASTYR UNIVERSITY EXPERIENCE

"Bastyr was more than a springboard for me; it was a rocket launcher."
— Michael Murray, ND ('85)

"I really can't imagine another place where you can leave medical school with such a vast collection of tools to help people with their health."
— Chris Krumm, ND ('04), MS ('04), LAc

"There were many things I loved about Bastyr: the cutting-edge curriculum, the beautiful campus, the invigorating buzz that filled the air. However, what I appreciated most was the incredibly bright, experienced, and dedicated faculty."
— Darcie Boltz, BS ('07) health psychology

"Bastyr is at the forefront of the natural medicine revolution."
— Kristen Spitz, ND, LAc ('12)

"We learn to take the health of the whole person into account at Bastyr."
— Nadia Kharas, ND ('13)

"We learn to empower people to create health for themselves."
— Heather Sandison, ND ('13)

"Natural practices seem to be more helpful in the long term. We're actually curing something, instead of just treating the symptoms. We're looking at the whole body. In Chinese medicine, the acupuncture channels and organs are all connected. That makes sense to me."
— Yeeshen Tien, MS ('13), LAc

Top: *ND graduates, Class of 1990*
Left: *ND graduates, Class of 1991*

"As soon as I drove down the campus drive on my visit, with the trees arching over it, I knew that this was where I was supposed to be."
—Alexis Durham, BS ('08) herbal sciences

A road through the lush forest leading to the Kenmore campus

BASTYR CENTER FOR NATURAL HEALTH

By creating teaching clinics for graduate students in Seattle and in San Diego, Bastyr has made high-quality, affordable care available to thousands in these two urban centers.

In Seattle's Fremont/Wallingford neighborhood, Bastyr Center for Natural Health is the largest natural health clinic in the Pacific Northwest, with approximately 35,000 patient visits annually. Graduate students studying naturopathic medicine, acupuncture, nutrition, counseling, and ayurveda get hands-on patient care experience.

The clinic follows a "Team Care" approach. Patients benefit from the combined education, training, research efforts, and experience of a licensed health professional, plus two advanced student clinicians. A clinical supervisor is intimately involved with each patient's case and approves all diagnoses and treatment plans.

Bastyr also provides basic natural health care for diverse, often underserved, populations throughout the Puget Sound region. Through prearranged community care sites, advanced naturopathic medicine students and acupuncture students provide free or reduced-rate care under the supervision of Bastyr clinical faculty. In an average year, the University's students see more than 3,500 patients at community clinics.

Above: *Patient case-review session*

Right: *Using electronic health records in exam room*

Bottom: *A young patient*

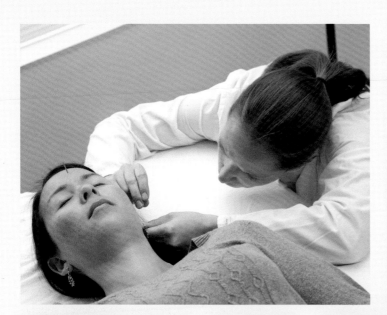

Clockwise from upper left: *Acupuncture treatment; Bastyr Center for Natural Health retail dispensary; educating a patient about herbs; Seattle clinic entrance*

CHAPTER FOUR

BRANCHING OUT

In its early years, JBCNM's core courses focused on natural therapies—nutrition, glandular therapy, botanical medicine, homeopathy, acupuncture, stress management, lifestyle counseling, and physiology. The common thread binding together these disciplines was a focus on *vis medicatrix naturae,* the healing power of nature. Faculty emphasized the healing of the whole person—body, mind, and spirit—and patients' participation in their own healing.

Out of this basic curriculum, new programs emerged. The school, now renamed Bastyr College, began offering bachelor's and master's degrees in nutrition in 1984. Nutrition is an integral part of naturopathic training, but many career opportunities for nutritionists do not require an ND degree.

Dr. Qiang Cao, then a student in the ND program, had an MD degree from China and was proficient in acupuncture and Oriental medicine. He began teaching acupuncture courses at Bastyr College in 1988. When the administration noticed that nearly 20% of the ND students were enrolling in these classes, the College decided to add a third degree program. The Master of Science in Acupuncture and Oriental Medicine (MSAOM) program was formally established in 1989. Dr. Chongyun Liu, also an MD (China), joined the faculty in 1991, helping to push the program forward.

Naturopathy and Midwifery

At the time Bastyr was founded, naturopathic physicians were licensed to practice under the 1919 Drugless Healing Act. This meant they were limited to

Left: *A lone tree stands vigil on the Kenmore campus*

IT'S A FACT

The first Bastyr University cookbook, From the Bastyr Kitchen, *was released in 2004.*

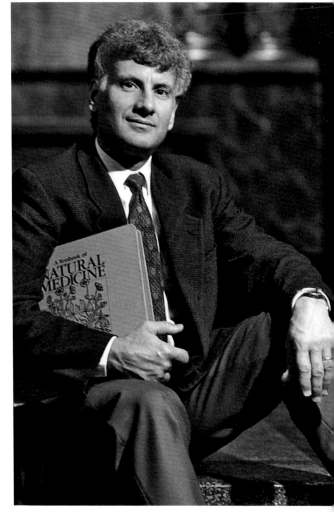

In 1985, Dr. Joseph Pizzorno published the Textbook of Natural Medicine *with co-author Michael T. Murray, ND*

the procedures allowed to "drugless healers" by the state law. As licensed "drugless healers," they could not legally deliver babies.

Childbirth, as practiced by MDs, often involved minor surgery, such as an episiotomy (a small cut made to enlarge the vaginal opening). While obstetrics and childbirth were part of the naturopathic curriculum, natural childbirth training did not routinely include minor surgery. However, anyone delivering babies had to be prepared to perform minor surgery, if necessary.

Dr. Griffith applied to be licensed as a midwife, but the state rejected his application on the basis that he was a graduate of a naturopathic college, not a school of midwifery. So Dr. Griffith sued the State of Washington, represented by attorney George Cody, then a Bastyr board member.

Cody argued before a state court judge that an ND program offered training comparable to the training that students received at the Seattle Midwifery School, preparing them to take the state's midwifery licensing exam. The judge ruled that Dr. Griffith could be licensed and allowed to teach midwifery, once he had passed the licensing examination.

The next exam was in three weeks. Drs. Griffith and Pizzorno quickly learned the terminology of midwifery, took the test, and passed, becoming licensed midwives. In 1982, Bastyr established a Certificate in Naturopathic

A new banner was unveiled in 1984 when the John Bastyr College of Natural Medicine was renamed John Bastyr College

Midwifery program for ND students interested in delivering babies. Eventually the state approved the program, which allowed direct licensing of NDs as midwives.

The Naturopathic Practices Act

Another problem with naturopathic doctors being licensed as "drugless healers" was that they could not legally perform venipuncture. Only licensed physicians were allowed to perform surgical procedures, and inserting a needle into a vein was considered surgery.

Because naturopathic doctors in Washington were not licensed as physicians, it was technically illegal for them to draw blood for routine lab tests. The first director of Bastyr's clinic, Dr. Charles Black, placed his own license on the line to teach venipuncture and supervise students drawing blood from patients, knowing that a modern clinical practice could not be created without this essential tool.

When the first class graduated from JBCNM in 1982, approximately forty practitioners were licensed to practice naturopathy in Washington; by November 1986 an official report to the Washington state legislature noted that 179 naturopaths were currently licensed to practice in the state. This increase of 140 or so new licensees was the direct result of students graduating from the College with ND degrees between 1982 and 1986.

But the legislative process to "sunset" licensing of naturopathic physicians under the Drugless Healing Act, which would become effective in 1987, was still in motion. Fortunately, part of that process was the Department of Licensing (DOL) and the Office of Financial Management (OFM) participating in the preparation of "sunset review" reports to go to the state legislature.

The DOL had experience working with Bastyr College; it had reviewed the school for compliance with the Washington Administrative Code and granted approval for graduates to apply for licensure. The department had worked with Bastyr College and a rejuvenated Washington Association of Naturopathic Physicians (WANP) flush with recent graduates to establish an upgraded licensing exam. In 1985 the DOL had recommended legislative passage of an amendment to the Drugless Healing Act adding clear authority for naturopaths to perform venipuncture (draw blood for diagnostic purposes).

Clockwise from above:
*The medical school's original
clinic was opened in Seattle's
University District; A sign
welcomes visitors to Bastyr
University's first home—
the former McDonald
Elementary School*

TRADITIONAL CHINESE MEDICINE

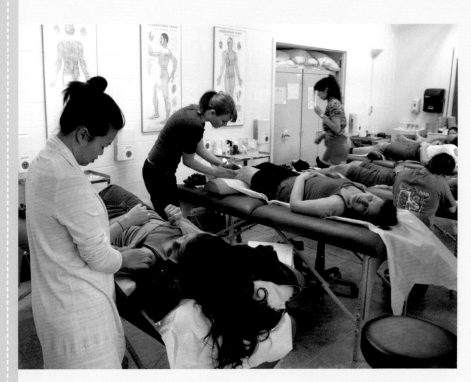

A Bastyr alumnus became the first acupuncturist for University of Washington (UW) Neighborhood Clinics in 2014. Iman Majd, MD, LAc, a 2005 graduate of Bastyr's acupuncture program, is a board-certified family medicine physician who sees patients at UW Neighborhood Factoria Clinic. He treats a broad range of conditions using acupuncture, supplements, and lifestyle therapies; many of his patients come through referrals from other UW physicians.

"Patient demand was a significant factor in the change," said Peter McGough, MD, medical director of UW Neighborhood Clinics. "There is high patient demand for acupuncture services and a growing body of evidence supporting its use."

Above and right:
Students participate in an acupuncture lab in the Department of Acupuncture and East Asian Medicine on the Kenmore campus

For more than twenty-five years, traditional Chinese medicine (TCM) has been part of the Bastyr University curriculum. The Department of Acupuncture and East Asian Medicine was formed in 1989 in response to growing interest in ancient Chinese medical techniques, such as acupuncture (the insertion of small metal needles into patients' skin and underlying tissues at key points in the body), herbal formulations, cupping, and massage.

Students at Bastyr receive rigorous classroom and clinical training from some of the world's premier Chinese medicine educators. Graduates of the Master of Science in Acupuncture and Master of Science in Acupuncture and Oriental Medicine programs are eligible to apply to become licensed acupuncturists (LAcs) in Washington state, as well as in most other states offering similar licensure. In 2014, acupuncturists were licensed to practice in forty-four U.S. states and the District of Columbia.

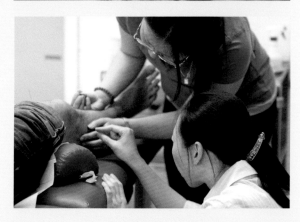

Together the DOL, Bastyr College, and the WANP proposed legislative language that established the basis for a modernized Naturopathic Practices Act. They met opposition from some MDs, who warned of "unproven medical practices," though the Washington State Medical Association chose to remain politically neutral. Still, the legislation was adopted during the legislative session of 1987, effective January 1, 1988. The language of the new act reflected the naturopathy curriculum at Bastyr College and the scope of practice encompassed in the *Textbook of Natural Medicine.*

The Long Road to Accreditation

The founders believed that for Bastyr to be perceived as a legitimate institution of higher education, it needed full accreditation, but in 1978, no accrediting agency existed for U.S. naturopathic colleges. No such college had ever been accredited. Bastyr had been approved by the Washington State Council on Post-secondary Education to operate as an institution of higher education—and had been certified by the Veterans Administration, so veterans could enroll—but accreditation was a different matter.

Voluntary peer accreditation would attest to the quality, competency, and authority of the institution to offer degree programs. Therefore, the College would have to meet the accreditation standards established by the Northwest Association of Schools and Colleges (NASC), one of seven regional accreditation organizations recognized by the U.S. Department of Education.

Bastyr took the first step by obtaining "preliminary candidate" status in 1980. BCNM's "Candidate for Accreditation" status was formally recognized in a letter from the NASC dated June 17, 1983. Bastyr was the first college of naturopathic medicine to ever receive such approval anywhere in the world. The new status made it possible for federal financial aid to come to students through Bastyr and be applied to Bastyr classes. It also enabled Bastyr to enroll foreign students, once it had approval by the Department of Justice and U.S. Immigration Service.

Yet, gaining full accreditation would take Bastyr four more years. At first the issue was whether Bastyr was a "single-purpose institution." After Bastyr was approved to be a candidate, the NASC appointed a committee

to reconsider their eligibility criteria. Some at Bastyr thought this was done in response to political pressure. Under new rules, the NASC categorized single-purpose institutions as trade schools, not colleges or universities. The association considered Bastyr "single purpose" because it offered only one degree program—naturopathic medicine. However, once Bastyr added a degree program in nutrition, which did not lead to an ND degree, the College no longer fell into that category.

Still, Bastyr met with resistance. In 1986, the NASC changed some of its qualifying language. The new language stated that the association would no longer accept applications from institutions "whose *primary* purpose is highly specialized *professional* education" (italics added). Interestingly, Bastyr College was the only school affected by the new definition.

Struggles over this provision lasted two years, but Bastyr College was finally granted full accreditation status in 1989, retroactive to September 1988. This was a

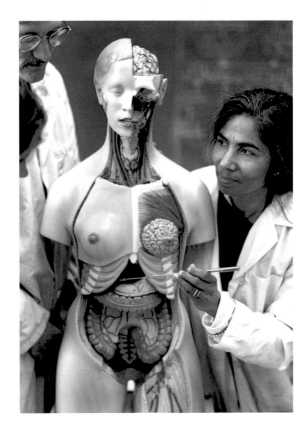

Aleyamma Thomas, PhD, teaches anatomy to ND students

CENTER FOR HEALTH POLICY AND LEADERSHIP

The nonpartisan Center for Health Policy and Leadership supports student visits to Congress each year to urge lawmakers to better recognize and integrate naturopathy into the nation's medical system

For almost four decades, Bastyr's founders and leaders have worked to build up professions such as naturopathic doctor, acupuncturist, and midwife. They've understood that training and education, while valuable, are not the only things needed for the practice of natural medicine. Licensing, scope of practice regulations, insurance coverage, and public understanding also play important parts.

In 2011, Bastyr launched the Center for Health Policy and Leadership (CHPL), a nonpartisan, University-based center dedicated to advancing the understanding of health policy and leadership issues. The CHPL has organized on-campus and external conversations on topics such as insurance regulation, the Affordable Care Act, and genetically modified foods labeling.

Groups of students travel to Capitol Hill each spring for the annual D.C. Federal Legislative Initiative (DC FLI), a three-day event of political leadership workshops and lobbying organized by the American Association of Naturopathic Physicians (AANP).

In 2013, Bastyr students and other AANP representatives approached U.S. House and Senate offices, seeking support for a Naturopathic Medicine Awareness Week. As a result, Congress designated October 6–12, 2014, as Naturopathic Medicine Week, recognizing the value of naturopathic medicine in providing safe, effective, and affordable health care.

More than fifty students from Bastyr participate in DC FLI annually, lobbying for legislation to better recognize and integrate naturopathic doctors into the current medical system. Members of the AANP visit more than 100 congressional offices to discuss the value of naturopathic medicine.

Annually, the Kenmore and San Diego campuses host legislative visitors. During the tours, students speak about their education and their chosen profession. Adam Silberman, ND candidate ('16), said, "Being able to walk Senator Marty Block through our clinic—explaining our philosophy of care and strong clinical training—brought me a sense of pride and excitement. How we are learning to work with patients will transform health care."

historic event. Bastyr became the first accredited naturopathic institution of higher education not just in the United States, but in the world.

As tedious and lengthy as the accreditation process was, it brought benefits beyond greater credibility with the public. The process helped to create accreditation standards for the naturopathic profession. As part of the American Association of Naturopathic Physicians, Dr. Pizzorno helped resurrect the Council on Naturopathic Medical Education (CNME), which had gone on hiatus. In 1987 U.S. Secretary of Education William Bennett approved the CNME as the accrediting agency for educational programs that lead to an ND degree. The CNME would accredit six other colleges of naturopathic medicine in the United States and Canada by 2014.

The accreditation process also provided Bastyr with a blueprint for institutional development and excellence. Three other U.S. colleges of natural medicine, started around the same time as Bastyr, did not survive. None had sought accreditation.

Early Financial Struggles

From the beginning, Bastyr's leadership was visionary and passionate, but a lack of sufficient funds limited what could be accomplished. There wasn't enough money for hiring student financial-aid staff, expanding the library, starting a research center, and adding administrative staff and full-time faculty.

The College's leaders were novices at fundraising. Their early efforts mainly consisted of soliciting donations from practicing naturopathic doctors, a group of approximately 1,000 nationwide—an insufficient donor base, given the amount of money Bastyr needed. They also tried hiring a fundraising firm, but the results were disappointing.

In a 1981 report, Bastyr noted that its financial growth was "slow and painful." The school's operating budget for 1982–1983 was $700,000. Its goal for the 1985–1986 academic year was $1,040,000.

The leaders knew what the problem was: few people had heard of Bastyr College—it was too new—and the public knew little about naturopathic medicine. To come up with solutions, the school recruited John Weeks, who had a background in journalism and extensive political and civic connections, to work part-time on development.

Under Weeks's leadership, Bastyr launched strong public-education and community-relations campaigns. The faculty and staff began presenting public programs on naturopathic medicine through a speakers' bureau, and they developed a presentation explaining insurance issues. Weeks prepared news releases for the local media and a quarterly newsletter for patients and friends of Bastyr; he also helped Bastyr connect with eminent local philanthropists and supporters.

The first year, Weeks raised an amount equal to the costs of his travel. The second year, he brought Dr. Pizzorno with him, and together they garnered about $50,000 in donations. By the time Weeks left Bastyr, they were raising over $150,000 a year, some from companies making multi-year commitments of as much as $10,000 a year. By current standards this may not seem like much, but at the time it was a huge boon for the growing institution.

In 1984, Bastyr began receiving grants from small, family-owned foundations. Introductions to these foundations often came through grateful patients of the teaching clinic or members of the Board of Trustees. The first ones were a $6,000 grant from the Titcomb Foundation (a Pacific Northwest family foundation), and a $3,000 grant from the Seattle Foundation (an umbrella organization for numerous smaller family foundations). Once Bastyr had a track record of receiving some grants, other foundations considered Bastyr a potential grant recipient.

By the 1985–1986 academic year, Bastyr College's annual campaign had attracted 400 donors, 75% of whom were new. It worked as a grassroots campaign, run by students, trustees, and alumni. Contributions came from twenty-seven states. Total contributions averaged around $50,000 per year—a good foundation for future growth.

47

BASTYR LIBRARIES: PAPER, DIGITAL, HUMAN

The Bastyr University Library has the most extensive collection of materials relating to the natural health sciences in the Pacific Northwest. Within the library are 19,000 books on topics ranging from nuitrition, acupuncture, botanical remedies, and naturopathic medicine to qigong and Zen meditation. Other works include basic medical texts in anatomy, physiology, and physical diagnosis. The library subscribes to 250 journals from the United States and abroad, covering all aspects of medicine. Its historical collection and archives contain many early and rare items.

Bastyr students also have access to specialized and general medicine databases, such as Access Medicine, the American Botanical Council database, PubMed, and the Traditional Knowledge Digital Library. Hundreds of naturopathic, nutritional, and botanical association conference proceedings, lectures, and documentaries are available in a variety of formats.

One day a year, student clinicians learn from a very different type of library. The Michelle Eustache Human Library is a training event that helps future doctors explore prejudices and dispel stereotypes they may have when encountering diverse patient populations.

Held at Bastyr Center for Natural Health, the human library is a living, breathing group of volunteer participants, known as "books," each representing different marginalized or less familiar identities. Among the guests who have appeared as "books" are people who are HIV-positive, blind and deaf, Muslim, transgender, and non-native speakers of English.

Bastyr students talk with these "books" and ask them questions, with the goal of demystifying preconceived notions and learning to become culturally competent health care providers.

"We are very excited about the Human Library project as an innovative way to promote diversity training for Bastyr University students," said the event organizer, Dan Rosen, PhD, associate professor in the Department of Counseling and Health Psychology. "Getting our students

Right: A teaching model in the library stacks, Kenmore campus

Upper Left: *Kenmore Library*

Left: *The Human Library project, a training event, helps future doctors explore prejudices and dispel stereotypes they may have when encountering diverse patient populations*

out of their comfort zones in order to become educated about marginalized and oppressed communities is the most effective way to learn, and is a bold but necessary step in their development as future health professionals."

CHAPTER FIVE

GREEN LEAVES

Throughout the 1990s, Bastyr College grew organically, taking advantage of many unexpected opportunities. While it remained rooted in the core values of its founders, the College extended its community outreach and influence through collaboration and partnerships. Beyond the naturopathic community, Bastyr formed partnerships with government, community agencies, businesses, and individuals. These helped shape the young school's future. To survive, much less thrive, the College could not go it alone.

Research in the Natural Arts and Sciences

From the start, Bastyr's leadership understood the importance of scientific research to support its curriculum. Initially, funds for research were hard to find. Bastyr was too new to attract government, foundation, or private funding. With the establishment of the Bastyr Research Center in 1986, the College took on the challenge of pioneering natural health research.

Bastyr's first major undertaking was the Healing AIDS Research Project, started by the new center's director, Leanna Standish, ND ('91), and fellow researcher Jane Guiltinan, ND ('86). The AIDS epidemic had become so virulent that the medical establishment was open to exploring a wide range of potential new therapies. This pilot study, completed in 1990, focused on a small group of patients with AIDS symptoms.

Sixteen patients participated in the study for a full year without taking azidothymidine (AZT), the first U.S. government-approved treatment for HIV. The

Left: Alchemilla vulgaris, *lady's mantle*

researchers studied how people with AIDS responded to vitamin C and beta carotene, herbal remedies including glycyrrhiza, heat treatments, nutritional counseling, and psychotherapy.

"Our concentration," Dr. Standish explained in an interview with *The Seattle Times*, "is on the idea that [AIDS virus infection] is a chronic, manageable condition. It is not a death sentence. . . . We also talk about the needs of the body, mind, and spirit—all three levels of existence."

It wasn't a controlled study, because patients with AIDS didn't want to be part of a control group not receiving any treatment. Still, the results were encouraging: participants reported reduced symptoms such as fatigue, swollen lymph glands, chronic diarrhea, and night sweats.

The Healing AIDS Research Project would prove instrumental in Bastyr becoming the nation's first natural medicine institution to receive a grant from the National Institutes of Health (NIH). In 1994 the federal Office of Alternative Medicine (OAM) awarded Bastyr an $840,000 three-year grant to fund the creation of an alternative medicine research center on AIDS. This was a landmark accomplishment: no naturopathic college anywhere in the world had received a government grant to create a research institute.

Bastyr's AIDS Research Center would go on to collaborate with the National Institute of Allergy and Infectious Diseases (NIAID), studying the outcomes associated with alternative medicine use among almost 500 HIV-positive participants.

The Bastyr Research Center was renamed Bastyr University Research Institute (BURI) in 1994. Faculty members and research scientists have studied the effectiveness of natural medicine treatments on hepatitis C,

diabetes, cardiovascular and brain disorders, and cancers of the prostate, ovaries, and breast. By 2015, more than 100 studies in a range of areas, including botanical and homeopathic medicine, had been completed or were under way.

New Acceptance in Washington State— and Washington, D.C.

Health care reform was a major legislative issue in U.S. federal and state governments in the late 1980s and early 1990s, due to skyrocketing costs. Bastyr's work educating local, state, and federal legislative leaders about the College and about naturopathic medicine was about to pay off, in the form of unprecedented opportunities for productive, reputation-building collaboration.

Deborah Senn's election in 1992 as Washington state's first female insurance commissioner ushered in a wave of support for the naturopathic community. Senn had been seeing a naturopathic physician regularly and recognized the value of complementary and alternative medicine. One of her first official acts was appointing a stakeholder committee to advise her on health care reform. She named John Weeks, by then Bastyr's vice president for external affairs, as the committee chair.

Having campaigned on the need for health care reform in Washington state, she leveraged work started by Governor Booth Gardner. His Health Services Commission introduced the Washington Health Services Act, which the state legislature enacted in 1993.

Deborah Senn was able to add an "every category" provision to the act before it came up for a vote. This provision required that all categories of licensed health professionals, including naturopathic doctors, be included in health insurance plans as long as they stayed within the scope of practice designated by the profession and the licensing agency.

The reform was short-lived. When the winds of politics reversed direction, the Washington Health Services Act was largely gutted the following year. Efforts led by Senn saved the "every category" provision, which became law in 1996. It was immediately challenged in court. In 2000, the state Supreme Court declared the provision constitutional, and Washington became the first state to require that complementary and alternative providers be included in insurance plans.

Meanwhile, natural medicine was beginning to move more into the national mainstream. A 1990 national study organized by David M. Eisenberg, MD, of Harvard Medical School found that one in three respondents (34%) reported using at least one unconventional therapy (such as relaxation techniques, chiropractic treatments, massage, spiritual healing, or commercial weight-loss programs) in the past year; a third of these saw providers for so-called "unconventional therapies." From the study results, published in the *New England Journal of Medicine* in 1993, Eisenberg extrapolated that in 1990 Americans made an estimated 425 million visits to providers of unconventional therapies, a number that exceeded the number of visits to all U.S. primary care physicians (388 million).

In 1992, the Office of Complementary and Alternative Medicine (CAM) was established within the National Institutes of Health (NIH). In 2014, the Office became the National Center for Complementary and Alternative Medicine (NCCAM), with much more substantial funding. The political push to turn the "office" into a "center" was created by a loose coalition of natural health professions. Leadership for the coalition included Pamela Snider, ND ('82), and Bastyr co-founder Sheila Quinn, who co-authored with two other colleagues a national plan to integrate CAM disciplines into the nation's health care system. Snider and Quinn made several trips to Washington, D.C. to meet with politicians and urge them to support the new center.

The following year, Dr. Pizzorno was appointed to the Advisory Panel on the Safety and Efficacy of Dietary Supplements within the Congressional Office of Technology Assessment. When First Lady Hillary Clinton was working on health care reform legislation, Dr. Pizzorno was one of only four natural health leaders invited to recommend to the steering committee how natural medicine should be incorporated into the federal health care system. In 2000, President Bill Clinton appointed him to the White House Commission on Complementary and Alternative Medicine Policy.

King County Clinics

In 1994, four men approached the King County Council with what was then a radical proposal. Dr. Pizzorno, John Weeks, Bastyr faculty member Jeffrey Bland, PhD,

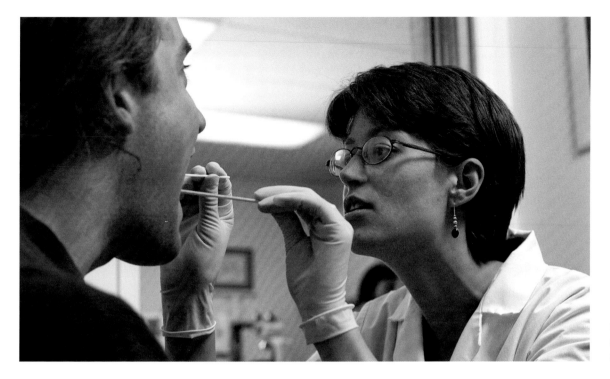

A clinician cares for a patient at Bastyr University Natural Health Clinic, mid-1990s

and Jonathan Wright, MD, who worked at a community clinic in Tacoma, proposed starting a naturopathic clinic in the publicly funded King County Community Health Centers. It would provide treatment for low-income patients while enabling the county to compare the effectiveness of conventional medicine and natural therapies.

The timing was perfect; increasingly, patients at the community health centers were expressing interest in complementary and alternative medicine. The proposal to add an integrative medicine clinic was approved unanimously. The Council then directed the Seattle/King County Department of Public Health to prepare a request for proposals to manage the new clinic.

Competition was stiff from Harborview Medical Center and Pacific Medical Center and Clinics, but in July of 1996 Bastyr was awarded a contract to operate the King County Natural Medicine Clinic—the nation's first government-run natural medicine clinic—in collaboration with the Community Health Centers of King County.

Media interest was intense when the Bastyr-run clinic opened as part of the Community Health Center in Kent, an ethnically diverse area south of Seattle. Journalists flew in from all over the country. More than 1,500 news stories were reported, by *Good Morning America* and *The New York Times,* among other national media, and local and regional newspapers. Not only had the King County Council approved the nation's first publicly funded natural medicine clinic, but it was also revealed that nine of the thirteen county council members had consulted complementary and alternative medicine providers.

Dr. Jane Guiltinan, who had been the medical director of the Healing AIDS Research Project, was put in charge of the new clinic. In 1999, she was appointed to the board of directors for Harborview Medical Center, the Northwest region's leading trauma center, becoming the first U.S. naturopathic physician to serve on a public hospital's board of trustees. When Dr. Pizzorno was named to the board of the Seattle/King County Department of Public Health, he became the first naturopathic doctor in the nation to be appointed to a board of public health.

Times were changing, and Bastyr was in the middle of that change.

TIERNEY RESEARCH LABORATORY

Above and right: *Bastyr and University of Washington researchers tested the effects of an extract from the turkey tail mushroom (facing page)—a traditional East Asian medicine—as a means of fighting cancer in concert with other conventional treatments*

n 2000, a large grant from Thomas and Elizabeth Tierney funded the creation of Tierney Basic Sciences Research Laboratory—the first research laboratory established at a natural health arts and sciences institution. The 2,500-square-foot high-tech facility on the Kenmore campus has made it possible for students and faculty to conduct experiments in analytical chemistry, immunology, cell and molecular biology, and biochemistry.

The laboratory enabled Bastyr to apply for basic-sciences grants it did not qualify for previously. As of 2014, the general focus of research was cancer prevention and treatment, stimulation of the immune system, and the chemical characterization of botanical products.

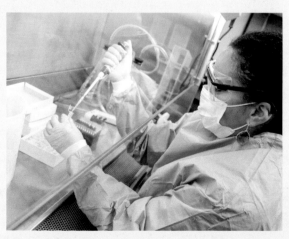

HYDROTHERAPY

Hydrotherapy, the therapeutic use of water, is a form of treatment that students learn early in Bastyr's Doctor of Naturopathic Medicine program. Besides home remedies many learn from their mothers—a bag of ice on a bruise, a hot bath after a long day—hydrotherapy offers natural ways to ease muscle soreness, relieve cough and flu symptoms, and reduce stress.

A 2014 renovation at the Kenmore campus included a new hydrotherapy lab, with bathing facilities, a sauna, massage tables, and hot and cold wraps. The lab is home base for the Nature Cure Club, a student group that practices fundamental naturopathic therapies through open lab sessions and field trips.

"I strongly believe in educating patients," said Hannah Gordon, who was president of the club in 2014. "I want to give my patients something they can do at home as a preventive way to support the fundamentals of health. If they get a sniffle, they know how to do a steam inhalation. They don't need to visit a doctor for that."

Modern hydrotherapy harkens back to the work of Sebastian Kneipp, a Bavarian priest born in 1821, who popularized the use of alternative temperatures and pressures of water to encourage healing. His "Kneipp Cure" was passed on by naturopathic leaders such as Benedict Lust and eventually was adopted by Seattle's Dr. Bastyr, the University's namesake.

Each September, a faculty-led group of Bastyr students spends two weeks in Germany studying the history of hydrotherapy. The Spa Medicine in Germany trip helps them learn about Kneipp hydrotherapy techniques, lymphatic drainage, connective tissue massage, sports therapy, and aqua wellness. Students also talk to practitioners about the German system of medicine, rehabilitation, and spa management.

Right: *Hydrotherapy is a treatment that has been documented for hundreds of years*

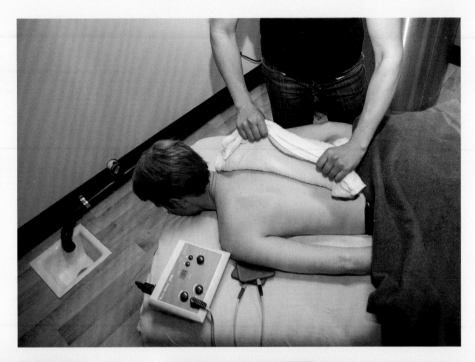

Nathan Petersburg and Hannah Gordon, both ND candidates, practice techniques in the hydrotherapy lab in Kenmore

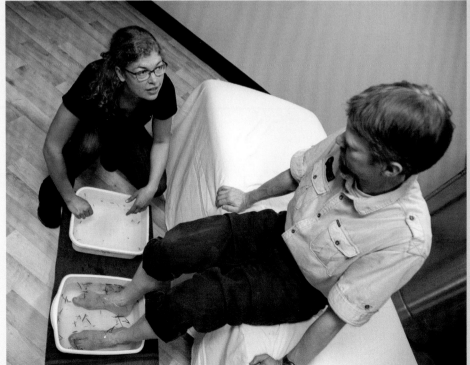

THE BASTYR UNIVERSITY EXPERIENCE

IT'S A FACT

The film score for Brokeback Mountain, *recorded in the Bastyr Chapel in 2006, won an Oscar for best original score.*

"Bastyr is such a special place! It provides a sense of community that has helped me grow in so many ways, intellectually and personally. I'm receiving an education I know I couldn't get anywhere else in the world."

—Danae Silva, BS ('14) nutrition

"Being in a state park every day is a lovely retreat from the bustle of the city."

—Kathryn Anderson, nutrition and exercise science student ('15)

"The professors do everything they can to allow you to succeed."

—Debra Daniels, BS ('14) integrated human biology

"The tranquil setting of the campus is a perfect complement to our studies."

—Kimberly Knight, nutrition/DPD student ('15)

Students and alumni gather for a weekend campout known as "Bastyr Revival"

"Everyone here has big hearts and bright visions. We are an integrated family of future leaders and supporters all striving to develop ourselves, serve our community, and promote natural health."

—Amy Jiang, acupuncture and Oriental medicine student ('16)

"The professors see students as future colleagues. Their job is to teach us to be the best we can be, considering we will be working alongside them in the future."

—Chloe Scheel, ND candidate ('16)

"San Diego makes living a healthy lifestyle very easy. You find hiking a mile from campus, surfing is nearby, yoga is everywhere, and natural health stores are more common than not."

—Natiya Guin, ND candidate ('16)

"I hope to take this knowledge and develop a holistic approach to my specialty as a dermatologist."

—Ushta Arayan, MD, PhD, MPH, ayurveda student ('16)

"The students are intimately connected, they care about each other, they look out for each other, they help each other grow, and they have gone through difficult moments together. They create a ferociously well-connected community that goes beyond some of our wildest dreams."

—Amy Davis, PsyD, counseling psychology clinical training director

Top: *ND graduates, Class of 1992*
Right: *ND graduates, Class of 2013*

CHAPTER SIX

BLOOM

From a small professional school with thirty-one students, Bastyr had grown by the mid-1990s into a much larger institution of learning and research, offering undergraduate, graduate, and doctoral degrees.

The Leadership Institute of Seattle (LIOS), an organization offering experiential programs in counseling, coaching and leadership development, became affiliated with Bastyr in 1992. Through the collaboration, which would last until 2009, Bastyr established a School of Applied Behavioral Science and offered Bachelor of Science and Master of Arts degrees with two tracks: systems counseling, and consulting and coaching in organizations.

For almost a decade, Bastyr had offered bachelor's degrees and master's degrees in nutrition. The school introduced a Didactic Program in Dietetics (DPD), which was approved by the American Dietetic Association in 1993. This program allowed students to complete their DPD while pursuing a Bachelor of Science with a Major in Nutrition. Graduation from the DPD program qualified students to apply for a dietetic internship; once they had completed the internship, they could take the examination to become registered dietitians (RDs).

To acknowledge its expansion into a multidisciplinary institution, the school took a new name in 1994: Bastyr University.

International Sister Schools

Bastyr University launched a Certificate in Chinese Herbal Medicine in 1994. As its acupuncture program expanded, more students wanted opportunities to

Left: *Aerial view of Kenmore campus and Saint Edward State Park*

IT'S A FACT

University enrollment in 2014-15 : 1,210

study in China and gain clinical experience there. That same year, Bastyr's leaders finalized its first "sister-school" agreement with Chengdu University of Traditional Chinese Medicine in southwest China. Founded in 1956, Chengdu is considered one of China's top traditional medicine universities.

Externships in China gave students in acupuncture programs a much different clinical experience than they would find closer to home. Western medicine and traditional medicine have been successfully integrated in China. At Chengdu, the faculty routinely prescribed therapies ranging from herbal medicine to chemotherapy. Visiting Bastyr students worked rotations in both inpatient and outpatient settings and typically saw three times the number of patients they would see on an average day in the United States.

In 2001, Bastyr established a second sister-school agreement, with Shanghai University of Traditional Chinese Medicine. Students in the University's graduate acupuncture programs could earn course credit by spending four weeks studying and working at one of the two Chinese universities.

A New Home

When President Pizzorno attended the first John Bastyr College of Naturopathic Medicine graduation in 1982, he looked around at the Saint Thomas Center's former seminary buildings and grounds and dreamed that it might become the College's future home. What better place for students to study natural medicine than on this beautiful fifty-one-acre campus in Kenmore, fourteen miles north of Seattle and adjacent to Saint Edward State Park on the northeast shore of scenic Lake Washington?

From 1999 through 2014, 687 weddings took place in the Bastyr Chapel.

Bastyr University founders mark the purchase of its fifty-one-acre campus from the Catholic Archdiocese of Seattle in 2005

The campus grounds, mid-1990s

Dr. Pizzorno's dream came true fourteen years later, when Bastyr University leased the property from the Catholic Archdiocese of Seattle. The move was a strategic one, helping ensure the school's growth and sustainability. By 1995, the University's population had exceeded 900 students and 125 faculty members. The annual operating budget was $6 million. Relocating from the cramped space at McDonald Elementary School in Seattle to the former seminary site, in what was then unincorporated King County, enabled Bastyr to accommodate its growing student body and expand its facilities.

The move took place in 1996. The teaching clinic (renamed the Bastyr University Natural Health Clinic) remained in Seattle's Wallingford neighborhood, but the Bastyr University Research Institute moved to Kenmore with the rest of the school. The addition of the high-tech Tierney Basic Sciences Research Laboratory in 2000 made it possible for Bastyr to play a larger role in scientific research in the natural health sciences.

At the Kenmore campus, the main University library had room to expand. By this time, the library offered the most comprehensive collection of clinically relevant natural health arts and sciences resources in the Northwest. Its growing collection was still small but was highly focused, including 6,000 volumes, 125 journal subscriptions, specialized audiovisual materials, and a suite of online medical and science databases.

The relocation also made more student amenities possible: a full-service vegetarian cafeteria, a bookstore, a non-denominational chapel, laboratory classrooms, an exercise laboratory, and ample parking. And Bastyr could now offer student housing on a limited basis: sixty-two single rooms on two of the upper floors in the main building.

The natural setting of the campus reflected Bastyr's philosophical heart and soul—the understanding that nature is an essential element in the healing process. The site offered room for new, much larger gardens. The Medicinal Herb Garden was designed, cultivated, and managed by students and volunteers under the guidance of a highly experienced garden manager.

Another advantage was the opportunity for diverse outdoor activities, an important facet of good health. Wooded hiking and biking trails linked Bastyr with trails through 316-acre Saint Edward State Park and to a secluded beach on Lake Washington. Students, faculty, and staff also had access to baseball fields and volleyball and tennis courts.

Top right: A yoga club gathering, Kenmore

Right: Class is held outside on a blue-sky day

Main entrance, Kenmore campus

By 1995, the University's population exceeded 900 students and 125 faculty members

Dr. John Bastyr, who cared for patients in the Seattle area for more than fifty years, died in 1995 at 83

Photo by Mark Frey

Saying Goodbye—and Hello

In June of 1995, the Bastyr community gathered at Saint Mark's Episcopal Cathedral in Seattle to mourn the passing, at age eighty-three, of John Bartholomew Bastyr, DC, ND, the school's namesake. At the memorial service, leaders in natural medicine, including Dr. Pizzorno, James S. Sensenig, ND, and Pamela Snider, ND, said goodbye to the beloved physician, mentor, teacher, and advocate.

One friend, Jim Ganzini, eulogized him this way: "In his devotion to keep alive the last school of naturopathy in North America, not unlike the last living tree of a species which bears fruit that falls away from the tree, he played a crucial role in propagating the profession, which was at that time nearly extinct. He was the root of a profession reaching back as far as any living physician of this era. He gave us a sense of history, longevity, stability and, above all, purpose. His having practiced until he could no longer was not only an inspiration, but showed us that the practice of medicine was a calling, a service, not just a job or a career. He was a leader in natural medicine,

not because of politics, but because he was the kind of human being we all strive to be."

Bastyr University was entering a new era. Three of the four founders had moved on. Dr. Mitchell had returned to teaching. Dr. Griffith, after serving on the Bastyr Board of Trustees for more than twenty years, left the state of Washington; he would later found the natural products company Nouvelle Health.

Sheila Quinn, who had been promoted to vice president in recognition of her outstanding work, left Bastyr in 1990. "Sheila's leaving left a big hole in the institution," Dr. Pizzorno recalled. "It took three people to take her place, and unfortunately the financial manager was not up to the task. Despite having maintained a balanced budget through all of Sheila's tenure, within a year of her leaving we faced a financial crisis."

Vice President Sandi Cutler recruited Sheldon Haber to become Bastyr's new vice president for finance. When Haber arrived, the University's payables were running over 120 days past due, and vendors would not extend credit to the school. "Sheldon was phenomenal," Dr. Pizzorno explained. "He cleaned up the mess, put good accounting systems into place, and brought us back on an even keel."

Like other nonprofit organizations and universities, Bastyr was governed by its president and board of trustees. The new position of executive vice president, with responsibility for day-to-day operations, was added in 1993. With this role filled by John Daley, PhD, a professional with extensive experience managing academic institutions, Dr. Pizzorno was able to focus on leadership development, strategic planning, external relations, public relations, legislative initiatives, and fundraising.

Other professionals were added to the staff, such as a director for the Office of Financial Aid. The University's budget grew by leaps and bounds. In 1993 the annual budget was $3,720,093; in 1998 it was $13,154,737. By 2003 Bastyr's budget had reached $22,662,023.

After faithfully serving as Bastyr's first president for twenty-two years, Dr. Pizzorno decided to leave the University in 2000 to promote new natural medicine-centric health care services in the corporate sector. The Board of Trustees began a nationwide search for a new leader who would empower Bastyr to build on its strengths, adapt to meet twenty-first-century challenges, and continue to be the leading innovator in natural medicine.

CONNECTING WITH THE WIDER WORLD

Acupuncture students pause for a photo during an externship in China in 2014

People come from all over the world to study at Bastyr's two campuses. In 2014, people were enrolled from thirty-one countries.

At the same time, one way the University prepares students to use their healing skills is by sending them out into the world. Some of their most powerful, formative experiences happen beyond the Kenmore and San Diego campuses.

Students pursuing their master's degrees in acupuncture travel to Chengdu University of Traditional Chinese Medicine or Shanghai University of Traditional Chinese Medicine, where they attend lectures and shadow senior doctors.

Nicolette Sakata, DAOM ('11), said the idea of integrating Eastern and Western medicine "really hit home during the externship." She came back to the United States with many ideas to integrate in her private practice.

"It's about combining traditional Chinese medicine and Western medicine in the best way possible to help people live longer with an improved quality of life," Sakata said, noting that in China oncology patients can receive "Western" chemotherapy one day and then, on a non-chemo day, take support herbs that help with the side effects. "This allows patients to continue their chemo regimen. Traditional Chinese medicine and Western medicine can work together the same way here in the U.S."

Other students learn about spa medicine and hydrotherapy in Germany; herbal medicine in Italy; and botanical medicine in Costa Rica.

Every other summer, a ten-day course explores early American uses of native plants in Appalachia. On the West Coast, students spend time camping and learning plant identification in the Cascades and harvesting seaweed in the San Juan Islands.

The Bastyr Student Council awards venture grants each quarter to send students on learning trips that promote personal and professional growth. Students design and propose the trips themselves and give a campus presentation when they return. Past grants have enabled students to study herbs along the Pacific Crest Trail, innovative retirement-home kitchens on Vancouver Island, and health systems in Ireland.

BASTYR UNIVERSITY CHAPEL

Built in 1958, the elegant Bastyr University Chapel features colorful mosaics, marble columns, stained glass windows, and hand-carved oak panels

Students and visitors stepping through the embossed copper doors sometimes gasp in surprise to find themselves in such a beautiful space. Built in 1958 as part of Saint Thomas the Apostle Seminary, the Bastyr University Chapel has a plain exterior but inside is rich with colorful mosaics, marble columns, stained glass windows, and hand-carved oak panels. Since Bastyr began leasing the property in 1995, the chapel has become a popular venue for weddings for people of all faiths, as well as the University's annual convocation ceremony, speaking engagements, professional music recordings, and concerts.

Donald B. Van Wieringen, the Seattle architect who was assigned to design the chapel, was instructed to make the space both visually elegant and as acoustically perfect as possible. Van Wieringen incorporated experiments into his design process and consulted with audio equipment and acoustics experts, with surprising success.

Musicians love performing in the chapel because of the way sound soars upward into the forty-eight-foot-high space but reverberates less than in most cathedrals. The chapel has hosted live concerts by the Oregon Symphony, Breath of Aire, Seattle Pro Musica, Kirkland Choral Society, the Seattle Jazz Singers, pianist and organist Burkard Schliessmann, organist Hector Olivera, and other performers. Even Hollywood has discovered Bastyr Chapel as a perfect place for music; the soundtracks for *Mr. Holland's Opus*, *About Schmidt*, *Brokeback Mountain*, Selma, and other movies were recorded here.

Left to right: *Close-up of high altar; A wedding in the chapel; Chapel roofline*

Below: *Annual convocation*

Left: *Perennial favorite Patrinell Wright, founder of the Total Experience Gospel Choir, sings*

Lower left: *President Church addresses a convocation marking the start of the 2014-15 academic year*
Below: *Organ music fills the 48-foot-high space*

Facing page: *A professional orchestra records music in the chapel*

BASTYR UNIVERSITY GARDENS

The Bastyr University Gardens next to the Student Village come to life each spring in the spring

A unique, student-maintained oasis of more than 350 medicinal and culinary plants, the Bastyr University Gardens play a central role in the education of Bastyr students. Those studying botanical medicine cultivate a variety of plants, which are harvested at their seasonal peak for use in medicinal tinctures and salves. Nutrition classes use the culinary herbs and organic vegetables in the University's whole-food kitchen laboratory and in the Bastyr Dining Commons. Excess harvests from the culinary crops are donated to a Hopelink food bank each summer.

At around 5,000 square feet, the garden is mostly organized by the body systems that the plants heal and support (i.e., cardiovascular system, musculoskeletal system). An exception is the Four Elements Garden, planted along the main garden's eastern edge in 2008 in honor of Robin DiPasquale, ND, a long-time professor and chair of the botanical medicine department. Paying tribute to the healing arts of the ancient Greeks, this small garden is arranged according to their classification system, associating herbs with the four elements of air, earth, fire, and water.

The public is invited to walk through the gardens' fragrant paths. Free guided tours are offered in the spring and summer.

Clockwise from top: Lavandula angustifolia, *lavender flower;* *Planting seeds begins a new cycle; Kuan Yin statue in garden; Plants receive tender, loving care from staff and students*

The annual Herb and Food
Fair is a unique and popular
event in the spring

Visitors marvel at the unique 5,000-square-foot garden, which is organized mostly by the body systems that the plants heal and support

THE BASTYR UNIVERSITY EXPERIENCE

"Bastyr's holistic, comprehensive approach to midwifery allows me to give women the care they deserve."

—Carlee Ann Brown, midwifery student ('15)

"Thanks to the integrated curriculum, an entire quarter's worth of knowledge flows together seamlessly in a way that makes it easily digestible. The academics at Bastyr are top-notch and will allow us to provide the highest quality of care to our patients in the future."

—Brenton Murphy, ND candidate ('17)

"I'm not only learning about nutrition, I'm learning about treating people with integrity and care."

—Ellie Freeman, MS, nutrition ('13)

"Bastyr University has played a bigger role within medicine than any other non-allopathic institution, bringing scientific legitimacy to natural medicine."

—James Wharton, PhD, professor of medical history and ethics, University of Washington School of Medicine

"I'm proud of our students and their academic achievements. Graduates of both our clinical and professional practice programs frequently outrank national averages in exam passage rates."

—Susan L. Weider, VP and dean of student services

Tibetan monks painstakingly create a sand mandala on the Kenmore campus

"My daughter is here today because of the fertility care I received at Bastyr Center."

—Danielle, acupuncture patient, Bastyr Center for Natural Health

"Bastyr University plays a significant role in the evolution of a fully integrative health care system, one with a focus on prevention and wellness; it offers its students innovative areas of study in the field of natural health, delivered with academic excellence and sensitivity to the health and well-being of each student."

—Leonard A. Wisneski, MD, FACP, Clinical Professor of Medicine, George Washington University Medical Center Faculty, Georgetown University and University of Colorado

"As Kenmore's largest employer, Bastyr University represents a tremendous asset and a springboard for natural health–related businesses that we want to encourage and grow. The City and the region benefit from the University's leadership and commitment to the community, and we are proud of our partnership."

—Rob Karlinsey, City Manager, City of Kenmore, Washington

"Naturopathic medicine is the future of medicine and Bastyr University is striving to bridge the gap between conventional medical knowledge and the heart of traditional healing—practical, holistic medicine focused on the individual. This is why I continue to support my alma mater."

—Lisa Chavez, ND ('07)

Top: *Midwifery cohort, 2013*
Bottom: *Commencement exercises, 2014*

BASTYR DINING COMMONS

Recognized with awards by *The Seattle Times* and *Evergreen Monthly*, the Bastyr Dining Commons offers an innovative whole-food menu for students, employees, and visitors alike. From tasty salad bar options, to creative hot meals and fresh-baked goods, the dining commons caters to a variety of diets, using sustainable ingredients and practices. Fresh herbs and vegetables are frequently harvested from the University's celebrated organic gardens. The space is also a popular place to gather, study, and connect with the Bastyr community. On any given day you might find a bake sale held by nutrition students, a garden sale featuring fresh veggies or special student-run events.

CHAPTER SEVEN

ABUNDANCE

In July 2000, the Board of Trustees selected Thomas Shepherd, DHA, to become the second president of Bastyr University. He came with more than twenty years of experience in hospital management and a personal commitment to integrative medicine.

"Bastyr is one of the world's leading centers of excellence in natural medicine. There is tremendous growth potential for both Bastyr and this medicine," President Shepherd told *Acupuncture Today*. "I believe that the current popularity of integrative medicine will continue, and that it is the wave of the future for American health care. I see the traditional delivery of health care changing fundamentally during my lifetime."

Self-Assessment and Reorganization

President Shepherd brought to the role new energy and determination to address issues that had been developing gradually over the years. He launched a new strategic planning process to examine the high turnover rate among faculty and administrators.

As a result, core faculty members' salaries were raised to match the national market averages for comparable positions at comparable independent academic institutions. Bastyr also increased health insurance benefits for the faculty and its retirement contributions for faculty and staff.

In 2001, almost half of Bastyr's courses were taught by adjunct faculty. The school was struggling to balance the needs of its successful naturopathic doctor (ND) degree program with the demands of added academic programs. Several of the core instructors were working more than 130% of full-time equivalency. To relieve

Left: Borago officinalis, *borage flower*

IT'S A FACT

Bastyr's first three presidents: Joseph E. Pizzorno, Jr., ND, 1978-2000; Thomas Shepherd, DHA, 2000-2004; Daniel K. Church, PhD, 2005-2015.

some of the workload, seven new core faculty members were hired during 2001 and 2002.

The University hosted its first "CAM Camp" in the summer of 2002. Funded through a collaborative National Institutes of Health grant, the summer program introduced University of Washington School of Nursing faculty to the basics of natural medicine. Later versions of the camp would bring conventionally trained medical students from across the country to Bastyr and its teaching clinic.

Part of President Shepherd's legacy was helping to lead the successful effort to bring the licensing of naturopathic doctors to California. He also helped to secure Bastyr's first million-dollar donation from an individual, California developer Stephen Bing, in 2002. The funds were used to build a state-of-the-art whole-food teaching kitchen, which was unveiled that year.

President Shepherd resigned in 2004 to take a corporate position on the East Coast, where he had deep roots. First John C. Daley, executive vice president since 1993, and then Schuyler W. Linninger Jr., chair of the Board of Trustees and its search committee, served as interim presidents while the trustees conducted a national search for Bastyr's next president.

A New President, A New Vision

On September 1, 2005, Daniel K. Church, PhD, took office as the third president of Bastyr. He not only had direct experience in the delivery of health care as CEO of Edwin Shaw Hospital in Akron, Ohio, but had been a tenured university professor with a PhD in communications theory and a firm belief in the importance of precise positioning—the need to refine the University's mission, vision, and message.

IT'S A FACT

Bastyr's economic impact on the Kenmore community in 2010: more than $136 million

Thomas Shepherd, DHA

President Church saw Bastyr's potential to transform how health care is viewed and practiced in our culture. Rather than being something people seek out only when they experience pain or illness, he believed that a concern for health should be fully integrated into people's lives. Health is not a commodity to be purchased from a doctor but a responsibility that our doctors and others can help empower us to accept, so that we live in ways that engender health rather than imperil it," he explained.

One way Bastyr could help Americans integrate good health into their everyday lives, President Church believed, was to more fully integrate traditional healing therapies with Western scientific practices. By working together, practitioners in these fields could learn from and influence each other.

It was time, as President Church put it, "to leave the bank and jump into the mainstream."

With this in mind, he pushed the University to shed its "alternative" label. Bastyr needed to focus instead on the *integrative* aspect of its mission, positioning itself as a collaborative leader in health care education.

The new president challenged Bastyr to re-examine its mission and vision with this integrative view in mind. After a strategic evaluation and planning process, the Board of Trustees adopted the following statements in 2007:

OUR MISSION

We educate future leaders in the natural health arts and sciences. Respecting the healing power of nature and recognizing that body, mind, and spirit are intrinsically inseparable, we model an integrated approach to education, research and clinical service.

OUR VISION

As the world's leading academic center for advancing and integrating knowledge in the natural health arts and sciences, Bastyr will transform the health and well-being of the human community.

These statements are posted in every classroom, office, and public space at the University—visible to the entire community and its guests. Yet a key member of the Bastyr community who would have appreciated these values was not present to see the University articulate them so clearly. Dr. Mitchell, one of the school's original co-founders, passed away suddenly and unexpectedly in January 2007.

The values and priorities encapsulated in Bastyr's

Daniel K. Church, PhD

Students enjoy the Kenmore campus grounds, early 2000s

new mission and vision statements would guide its leaders' decision-making as they strategically expanded operations. The University had added a Bachelor of Science with a major in Health Psychology to its offerings in 1998, a Bachelor of Science with a major in Exercise Science and Wellness program in 2000, and a Bachelor of Science with a major in Herbal Sciences program in 2001. The master of Science in Nutrition and Clinical Health Psychology came two years later. Now Bastyr launched a Bachelor of Science with a Major in Nutrition and Exercise Science, and a Bachelor of Science with a major in Nutrition and Culinary Arts.

After more than thirty years of training professionals in obstetrics, the Seattle Midwifery School merged with Bastyr in 2009, becoming the University's Department of Midwifery. The leaders of Seattle Midwifery School wanted to raise the standard of midwifery education by offering a degree program instead of a certificate, and decided that the best ways to accomplish this was by joining Bastyr. The following year, Bastyr University offered the nation's first accredited, direct-entry Master of Science in Midwifery program. Candidates entering the program with at least two years of undergraduate coursework (including Bastyr's prerequisites) could exit with a Master of Science in Midwifery in three years.

Sustainable Growth on the Kenmore Campus

More academic programs meant more students and faculty, and that meant classroom space and housing would be an issue. Where and how would these new programs and people be accommodated?

To expand, Bastyr needed a campus more permanent than a lease could provide. An opportunity presented itself sixty-seven days into President Church's administration. The University's lease with the Catholic Archdiocese of Seattle was scheduled to expire in 2006. The archdiocese offered a choice: Bastyr could either purchase the property on very favorable terms or sign a more expensive lease for twenty years. The University's leadership made the easy decision to buy the fifty-one-acre site for $8.5 million, with assistance from the Washington Higher Education Facilities Authority, which provided approximately $12 million in bond financing.

Once Bastyr owned the Kenmore campus, it could invest in remodeling and add more buildings. A high priority was additional student housing to enable students and families from outside the Seattle area to live on campus. The new Student Village was more than five years in the making but eventually provided

IT'S A FACT

For five years running (2009-2014), the Kenmore campus was recognized by the King County Solid Waste Division as one of the "best workplaces for waste prevention and recycling" in King County

living quarters for 132 students, when it opened in 2010.

While the new student housing was still under construction, Bastyr's leaders launched a transportation initiative to reduce the University's environmental footprint. The Kenmore campus, while close to Seattle, was not easily accessible by public transportation. Most of the students, faculty, and staff commuted by car.

Wanting to reduce its adverse impact on the environment and on traffic congestion on nearby Juanita Drive, a two-lane arterial through a residential neighborhood, Bastyr looked at ways of encouraging students and faculty to take public transportation, share rides, or bicycle to the campus.

Today Bastyr vans shuttle between the Kenmore campus and the University's teaching clinic in Seattle. Electric car charging stations installed on campus in 2011 accommodate low-carbon vehicles.

At the same time as they were making improvements in Kenmore, the University's leaders were planning something even bigger. For years there had been talk of opening a second campus. Under President Church, the idea was more fully researched and explored with encouragement from the California Naturopathic Doctors Association. Once a lease was signed on January 31, 2012, it became official: Bastyr was going to California.

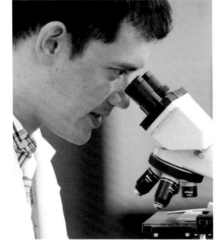

Clockwise from upper left: *Taking a closer look in a basic science lab; Herbal sciences student in the Botanical Medicine Lab; ND students practice minor surgical procedures*

The Turtle Pond Courtyard on the Kenmore campus is a popular gathering place

REFLEXOLOGY FOOT PATH

Smooth Northwest river rock is at the core of the sixty-five-foot-long Reflexology Foot Path, built in 2004

Adjacent to the Bastyr University Gardens is the Reflexology Foot Path, which was the first public, outdoor path of its kind in North America. The sixty-five-foot path, built in 2004, features smooth native Northwest river rock artistically embedded in cement.

Based on wisdom from ancient Egypt, India, and China, the reflexology path massages and stimulates acupressure points in the soles of the feet connected to various energy meridians of the body. The pressure of the stones under bare feet combines with gravity to provide a therapeutic exercise that is thought to stimulate health by detoxifying the body and relieving stress.

The path was designed by Elizabeth Marazita, a licensed acupuncturist who graduated from Bastyr in 2007 with a Doctor of Acupuncture and Oriental Medicine degree. She based the foot path on those commonly found throughout China and other Asian countries.

In her former life as an international banker who worked and lived in China for four years, Marazita first noticed a therapeutic walkway in Taipei, Taiwan, during a break from a business meeting. She watched an elderly man walk a path almost entirely composed of three-inch-high stones—an extreme difficulty level. "He was so serene," Marazita recalled in an interview with the *Seattle Post-Intelligencer*.

Bastyr's path is considered moderately difficult. A handrail and resting places along the path improve accessibility and provide a break for people who experience any discomfort. Marazita recommends drinking plenty of water in the hours after finishing the walk, to help flush out toxins.

Clockwise from right: *The foot path adjoins the Bastyr gardens; the foot path is considered to be moderately difficult with handrails and resting places*

NUTRITION DEGREE PROGRAMS

Bastyr University's nutrition programs begin with the whole picture, focusing on how nutrition affects not just one aspect of biology, but the entire spectrum of health. Nutrition students leave Bastyr with a comprehensive education that merges the science of nutrition with a much broader view of wellness, community, and the environment.

The pervasive emphasis on whole foods allows students to examine food in its entirety, from its individual components to how it affects the human body and human communities. Whether looking at nutrition through the lens of physiology, biomechanics, biochemistry, whole-food cooking, or health psychology, students learn how to support health from a variety of perspectives.

At the heart of study in Bastyr's Department of Nutrition and Exercise Science is the University's overarching focus on the interconnected nature of physical, mental, and spiritual health. Students working toward a Bachelor of Science in Exercise Science and Wellness, Nutrition, Nutrition and Exercise Science, Nutrition and Culinary Arts, or the Didactic Program in Dietetics, all experience training in whole-food education and whole-person health.

Master's-level degrees include Nutrition, Nutrition and Clinical Psychology, Dietetics, and Nutrition for Wellness, all of which prepare students for forward-looking careers in whole-food education, therapeutic nutrition counseling, research, writing, public speaking, and more.

A cutting-edge holistic approach is one of the hallmarks of the University, and means students are benefiting from something special. Bastyr's nutrition students and alumni are well poised to make a real difference in the health and wellness of communities now and into the future.

Right: *Delicious, healthy dishes flow from a kitchen that emphasizes the healing aspects of food*

Facing page: *Student Daniel Andras in the Nutrition Kitchen*

SUSTAINABLE STUDENT VILLAGE

Above and facing page:
*Student Village's 11
three-story buildings
house 12 students each
and became the first
student housing project
on the West Coast to
receive the highest-level
(platinum) certification
in the international
Leadership in Energy and
Environmental Design
(LEED) program*

In alignment with Bastyr's core belief that individual health and ecological health are inseparable, University leaders chose to emphasize environmental and social wellness not only in course curricula but also through the decisions they made in planning the Student Village. Promoting environmental responsibility and stewardship was central to the design and construction of the eleven three-story buildings.

The residences were designed to encourage social interaction; each one houses twelve students in private, single rooms with shared common spaces. The buildings fit into the natural landscape, and their impact on the environment was minimal due to features such as natural ventilation, radiant floor heating, high-efficiency boilers, low-flow plumbing, and Energy Star appliances. The buildings have distinctive "butterfly roofs" that

catch rainwater and reduce runoff pollution, and some support rooftop gardens.

When the Student Village opened in September 2010, it received Leadership in Energy and Environmental Design (LEED) platinum certification, the highest level of certification awarded for design, construction, and operation of high-performance green buildings, according to standards set by the U.S. Green Building Council (USGBC). This was the first time a student housing project on the West Coast had received the highest certification.

Two months later, the USGBC selected the University's innovative, eco-friendly village as the Outstanding Multi-family Project in the 2010 LEED for Homes Awards. On Earth Day, April 22, 2011, Bastyr was given a King County Green Globe Award for being a leader in sustainable building.

SAINT EDWARD STATE PARK

Adjacent to the Kenmore campus is the 316-acre Saint Edward State Park, a beautiful day-use park that offers the Bastyr University community and the public an elaborate network of bicycle and hiking trails and access to a remote beach on Lake Washington. A variety of wildlife and many species of birds, including bald eagles, are found among the Douglas fir, red cedar, big-leaf maple, madrone, and hemlock trees. The park is also home to the former Saint Edward Seminary, which is listed on the National Register of Historical Places.

Top: *Entrance to Saint Edward State Park*

Bottom: *The former Saint Edward Seminary, built in 1932, is listed on the National Register of Historical Places*

A canopy of trees creates a calming retreat near the campus

CHAPTER EIGHT

NEW SEEDS

In the Sorrento Valley north of downtown San Diego, Bastyr's leaders found the perfect location for a second campus. The site was in the center of the city's life sciences cluster, not far from the University of California San Diego Health System, Scripps Research Institute, Scripps Health hospital network, VA (Veterans Affairs) San Diego Medical Center, and several dozen clinical research organizations. It didn't hurt that the Sorrento Valley is close to stunning ocean beaches and coastal wild lands.

To house the second campus, Bastyr leased a two-story commercial building with ample classroom space. The building's design and zoning would allow the University to carry out laboratory and clinical education without major infrastructure investments or extensive permitting.

The University's market research had shown that Californians were keenly interested in integrative medicine. The state had a shortage of primary care physicians, a role that could be filled by naturopathic doctors (NDs). California was one of sixteen states that licensed NDs to practice as primary care professionals, thanks in part to the University's advocacy before the 2003 state legislature.

Bastyr University California

Bastyr University California opened on September 14, 2012. Approximately 400 current and prospective students, alumni, friends and members of the public attended the official ribbon-cutting. The celebrations included speeches from President Church; Mimi

Left: Eschscholzia Californica, *California poppy*

IT'S A FACT

In June of 2011, the online edition of U.S. News and World Report *included Bastyr University in its list of six "Colleges Catering to Vegetarians" in the United States*

Above right: In its first years the California campus offered a Doctor of Naturopathic Medicine program followed by a Master of Science in Nutrition for Wellness program

Guarneri, MD, director of the nearby Scripps Center for Integrative Medicine; and co-founders Dr. Griffith, Dr. Pizzorno, and Sheila Quinn.

The school's initial enrollment—forty-nine students from fourteen states—exceeded expectations. Everyone in the inaugural class was enrolled in the four-year Doctor of Naturopathic Medicine program; other programs, such as the Master of Science in Nutrition for

Wellness, would come later. Bastyr University Clinic, however, was open for business just ten days after the school's grand opening.

New Academic Offerings

On the Kenmore campus, meanwhile, the changes kept coming. In 2010, the University began offering a Certificate in Holistic Landscape Design. Bastyr is one of four schools in the nation to offer a certificate or qualification in sustainable landscape design, and it is the only such program that focuses on the therapeutic value of a medicinal and edible landscape.

Reflecting its focus on integrating medical traditions, Bastyr created a Bachelor of Science with a major in Integrated Human Biology program in 2012. In this program, students study the biological basis for human behavior and the connection between the human organism and the biosphere as a whole. That same year, a two-year, stand-alone Master's of Arts in Counseling Psychology was accredited and began enrolling students.

Bastyr added a Master of Science in Ayurvedic Sciences in 2013, the first such program to be accredited in the United States. Based on the 5,000-year-old medical traditions of India, ayurveda ("the science of life") combines nutritional counseling, herbal medicine, massage therapy and bodywork, internal cleansing, and immune system support.

In 2014, Bastyr University began accepting applications for two new graduate programs: Master of Public Health (MPH) and Master of Arts in Maternal-Child Health Systems.

Expanded Research Opportunities

Starting in 2008, the Bastyr University Research Institute began developing its potential in the field of cancer research. It launched the Bastyr Integrative Oncology Research Center (BIORC). By 2014, nearly 650 oncology patients in all stages of various cancers participated in Bastyr integrative oncology studies. A grant from Cleavage Creek Cellars, a producer of world-class wines that contributed 10% of its gross sales to fighting breast cancer, supported initial uncompensated patient care.

BIORC's existence led to Bastyr being awarded two major grants related to breast cancer research in 2010. The first was a $3.1 million National Institutes of Health (NIH) grant for Bastyr and the Fred Hutchinson Cancer Research Center to start integrative research on breast cancer.

This was followed by a $4.52 million grant to Bastyr and the University of Washington's Oncomycology Translational Research Center to study the effects of Polysaccharide Krestin (PSK) on breast and prostate cancer. PSK extract comes from the turkey tail mushroom (*Trametes versicolor*), a traditional East Asian medicine thought to both boost the immune system and fight cancer cells.

Another recent innovation was the Center for Student Research (CSR). Established in 2010, it's the central point of contact for students who want to conduct research. Joint student–faculty projects are funded through a competitive award process, which encourages students to develop their own research ideas.

One such idea led to a study of the important role of probiotics in combating antibiotic-resistant hospital

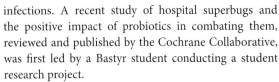

infections. A recent study of hospital superbugs and the positive impact of probiotics in combating them, reviewed and published by the Cochrane Collaborative, was first led by a Bastyr student conducting a student research project.

"The Center for Student Research made it possible for me to work on my research as a medical student. I've presented my research at conferences, where I've won awards and connected with researchers outside of Bastyr University. CSR provided opportunities for me to solidify my research education and gain confidence," said Renee Y. Choi, ND ('13), Natural Supplements Research Competition award recipient, 2013, and NIH training award grant recipient, 2010.

Reaching for the Future

As primarily a science-based graduate and professional university with relatively few undergraduate students, Bastyr wanted to offer its students more exposure to subjects such as the arts, politics, and history, which can help students become well-rounded human beings.

To compensate, the University developed centers of public conversation. The first, in 2009, was called the Center for Spirituality, Science, and Medicine. (It was later renamed the Center for Mind, Body, Spirit, and Nature.) It organizes academic electives and public events on topics such as contemplative practices in medicine, leadership, and compassionate social activism.

The following year, Bastyr launched the Center for Health Policy and Leadership (CHPL), a nonpartisan, University-based center that provides on- and off-campus opportunities for participation in "essential, generative conversations." The center hosts prominent scholars and health practitioners in discussion-oriented events; provides a forum for scholarly research on health policy and leadership issues; encourages citizens to participate actively in public affairs through programs that promote health and well-being; and publishes a blog on health care reform issues.

In February 2014, President Church announced that he intended to retire eighteen months later, after completing a decade of service as president of Bastyr University.

At the annual convocation ceremony in September, he delivered an inspiring message to the students about social justice.

"Don't just get jobs and careers—contribute to the promotion of a more just and humane society. Take on roles of leadership and service," said President Church, referencing the mission statement of Xavier University of Louisiana and applying it to the Bastyr community.

He then unveiled the Bastyr University Commitments, a list of five ideals developed by the Academic Leadership Council and the President's Cabinet: academic rigor, effective communication, respectful behavior, intercultural awareness, and social justice.

Specifically, President Church touched upon the inequities in health services, noting that 97.1% of U.S. health care spending is applied to half the population, leaving only 2.9% to meet the needs of the remaining 50%. He challenged Bastyr students to "remove the obstacles to cure," not only becoming excellent health care providers but also helping those with the greatest need in underserved communities.

As part of Bastyr's mission to prepare competent and confident leaders, President Church announced the establishment of a new Center for Social Justice and Diversity. Its work would begin on campus, infusing cultural competency and anti-racism education throughout classroom and clinical training at Bastyr. Besides improving cultural awareness, the center also would help students become engaged in efforts to seek social justice in the wider community.

"This is my last academic convocation as your president, and I cannot give up this bully pulpit until I have said as much as I can about what is on my mind," President Church concluded. "I hope you know how proud I am of all of you, and how confident I am that you will change the world for good."

A new president was called to Bastyr in 2015. Charles "Mac" Powell, PhD, became the university's fourth president. Dr. Powell came to Bastyr from John F. Kennedy University in Pleasant Hill, California, where he served as president.

A new chapter in the Bastyr University story had begun.

A student prepares medicinal tea in the botanical medicine lab on the San Diego campus

Above, right, and facing page: *Bastyr University California is equipped with a full complement of laboratory space and equipment for hands-on learning*

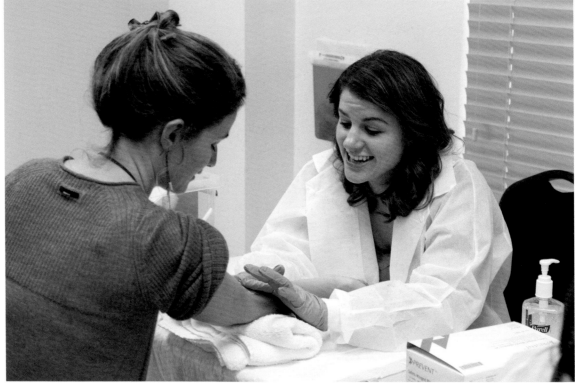

Students study
between classes

BASTYR UNIVERSITY CLINIC

Bastyr University Clinic, on the campus of Bastyr University California, opened in September 2012. A year later, the teaching clinic expanded with almost double the patient exam space, an IV/infusion room, a hydrotherapy room, a physical manipulation room, and a clinical preview room

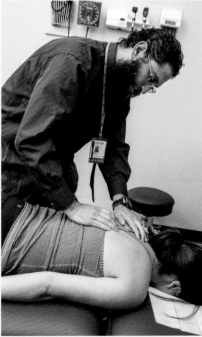

Cooking demonstrations
in the San Diego
Nutrition Kitchen

San Diego students visit the campus library, left, and practice cooking and botanical medicine making

San Diego students enjoy the sun at nearby Solana Beach

The San Diego campus is next to Los Peñasquitos Canyon, where students can access miles of trails

BASTYR CAMPUS TRADITIONS

Aerial view of the Kenmore campus

Throughout the year, students take breaks from their studies to enjoy some Kenmore campus traditions that celebrate the University's passionate, quirky culture.

SEPTEMBER. Fall quarter kicks off with the First Friday dance party, featuring free food and drinks, costumes, games, a DJ, and a photo booth.

OCTOBER. For Halloween, acupuncture students create "Haunted Trails," a nightmarish forest infested with ghosts, goblins, and monsters. One of the largest and most popular scare-fests in the area, it's a fundraiser for the University's China externships.

JANUARY/FEBRUARY. Bastyrians mark the first day of winter quarter with the "Splash and Dash": a run on the trails of Saint Edward State Park followed by a chilly dip in Lake Washington. Acupuncture students and faculty celebrate Chinese New Year by inviting classmates to qigong and tai chi sessions and a festive banquet. Students share their music, dance, juggling, comedy, and other talents (or lack thereof) at the annual Talent/No Talent Show.

MAY. On Community Day, afternoon classes are cancelled in both Kenmore and San Diego so students can get together for lunch, art projects, and games.

SPRING. As summer approaches, Bastyr welcomes thousands of visitors to its Herb and Food Fair, for live music, delicious food, garden tours, plant sales, kids' activities, and cooking demonstrations.

Left: *On the first day of winter quarter, daring Bastyr students make their way down a forest trail through Saint Edward State Park for a group jump—the Splash and Dash—into the chilly waters of Lake Washington*

Left: *Jubilant students hoist a trophy won in a competitive event on Community Day*

Right: *Kenmore students raise funds for the University's China externships with "Haunted Trails" in October*

TICKETS
- HAUNTED TRAILS
- HADE'S LABYRINTH
$20 - CIRCUS OF HORRORS
- CEMETERY HILL
- MUMMY'S TOMB

$5 FORTUNE TELLING

TRICK or TREAT
$5/CHILD CASH ONLY

KID'S CARNIVAL IN BUILDING
PRICING UPSTAIRS

Above: *A traditional mid-winter event in Kenmore is the Talent/No Talent show featuring skits, music, and other performances*

Right: *The Bastyr University campuses have many student organizations, including the Multicultural Association, which organizes various cultural performances*

On Community Day in the Spring, classes are cancelled on the two campuses to allow faculty and students to relax and have fun together

MIDWIFERY AND CHILDBIRTH-RELATED EDUCATION

Since Bastyr's early years, delivering babies has been an important part of the practice of many naturopathic physicians in Washington state. School namesake Dr. Bastyr is remembered as a highly respected midwife. Dr. Griffith, one of the school's co-founders, challenged the State of Washington for the right to be licensed as a midwife.

Bastyr began offering courses in midwifery in 1982. In 2009, the Seattle Midwifery School merged with Bastyr University, and the following year they established the only direct-entry Master of Science in Midwifery degree in the United States that was both regionally accredited and accredited by the Midwifery Education Accreditation Council (MEAC). Graduates of Bastyr's program meet the education and clinical training requirements to qualify to take the board exam to become certified professional midwives.

Initially a program of the Seattle Midwifery School, the Simkin Center for Allied Birth Vocations has become part of Bastyr's School of Natural Health Arts and Sciences. The center prepares students to serve as birth doulas, postpartum doulas, lactation consultants, and childbirth educators.

The Simkin Center is known for its world-class faculty, composed of leaders of the modern doula movement. Its namesake, Penny Simkin, PT, is credited with reviving the ancient art of providing continuous care in childbirth. Working with other health care providers, she adopted the term doula, a Greek word referring to an experienced woman who helps other women, and formed Doulas of North America (DONA), the birth and postpartum doula professional association that now has a global reach as DONA International.

Simkin has attended more than 800 births and trained more than 5,000 doulas around the world. After the merger between the Seattle Midwifery School and Bastyr, Simkin continued to serve as the center's senior faculty member.

"I care so much about all of those women I've helped over the years," said Simkin, who is known by many as the mother of modern childbirth education. "We've got to get people caring more about childbirth."

Top: *Students sit in on a lecture*
Bottom: *Students practice neonatal resuscitation techniques*

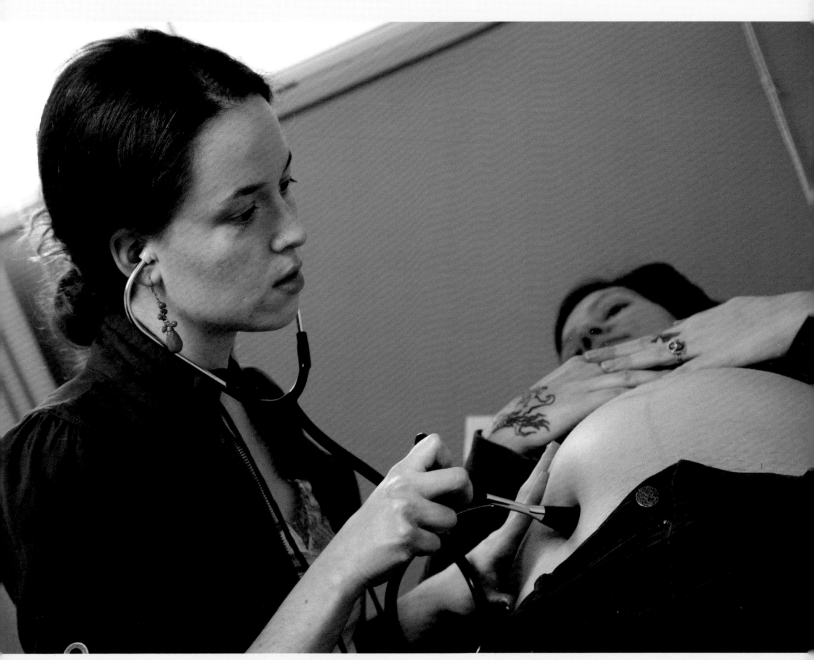

A student practices listening to a fetal heart rate

Penny Simkin conducts a birth doula class at the Simkin Center in Kenmore

SACRED SEEDS ETHNOBOTANICAL TRAIL

On June 2, 2012, Bastyr University officially introduced its new ethnobotanical trail at the fourteenth annual Herb and Food Fair, held at the Kenmore campus. Bastyr's trail is the only ethnobotanical trail on the West Coast affiliated with Sacred Seeds, an international project that helps communities stay connected to native plants; the next-closest official Sacred Seeds project is in Missouri.

The mile-long trail is designed to be used as a "living classroom" for teaching identification, seed saving, and cultivation of Pacific Northwest native species. It begins in a native plant meadow on the hillside behind the Bastyr University Gardens. From there, it passes through a grove of 100-year-old Douglas firs within the Student Village and into the woods, where it winds around to a wetland area. Signs identify native plants along the trail.

"We are honored to have been selected as the Pacific Northwest representative of the Sacred Seeds Sanctuary," said Sheila Kingsbury, ND, RH (AGH), chair of Bastyr's Department of Botanical Medicine. "This is a great opportunity to preserve, teach, and share what we know about native plants and why they have been, and continue to be, so important to our region."

*A spring rainbow crowns
the Kenmore campus*

SELECTED SOURCES

Most of the details in this history of Bastyr University were provided by primary sources in the Bastyr community. The authors of this book wish to thank the following people for their contributions of time, energy, and essential information: President Daniel K. Church, PhD; Martha G. Lynn, director of marketing and media; Adam Staffa, digital marketing specialist; Jane D. Saxton, MLIS, director of library services; Erin Aselas, director of institutional effectiveness; Timothy C. Callahan, PhD, senior vice president and provost; Sheldon R. Haber, vice president for finance and administration; Pamela Vaughn, director of conference services; Joseph E. Pizzorno, Jr., ND, founding president emeritus; co-founder Sheila Quinn; co-founder Les Griffith, ND; Pamela Snider, ND, executive editor of the Foundations of Naturopathic Medicine Project; and George W. Cody, attorney and former member of the Bastyr University Board of Trustees.

Alexander, Brian. "Naturopathic Physician, Co-Founder of Bastyr University" [Obituary for Dr. William Mitchell Jr.]. *The Seattle Times*, January 27, 2007. Accessed at http://seattletimes.com/html/obituaries/2003543647_mitchellobit27m.html.

Bastyr University. *Bastyr University Founders' Story—Complete Version* [video]. Recorded June 19, 2003.

Bastyr University. "University Leader Makes 'Integrative' a Hallmark of Career." *San Diego Business Journal* supplement. October 2012. Accessed at http://www.bastyr.edu/sites/default/files/images/pdfs/Marketing/Basytr_San_Diego_Business_Journal_supplement.pdf.

Birkland, David. "Dr. John Bastyr, 83, Renowned For Naturopathic Medical Skill." *The Seattle Times*, July 1, 1995. Accessed at http://community.seattletimes.nwsource.com/archive/?date=19950701&slug=2129107.

"Dr. Tom Shepherd Named President of Bastyr University." *Acupuncture Today*. August 2000 (Vol. 1, Issue 8). Accessed at http://www.acupuncturetoday.com/mpacms/at/article.php?id=27532.

Gazella, Karolyn A., and Suzanne Snyder. "Joseph Pizzorno, ND: Advancing the Field of Natural Medicine." *Alternative Therapies in Health and Medicine*. Jul/Aug 2006 (Vol. 12, No. 2): 54-60. ProQuest document ID 204832902.

King, Warren. "AIDS-Treatment Alternatives Tested—Healthful Diet, Exercise Focus of John Bastyr Study." *The Seattle Times*, November 7, 1990. Accessed at http://community.seattletimes.nwsource.com/archive/?date=19901107&slug=1102730.

King, Warren. "Bastyr Gets Grant For AIDS Research—U.S. Picks Area School That Studies Healing." *The Seattle Times*, October 4, 1994. Accessed at http://community.seattletimes.nwsource.com/archive/?date=19941004&slug=1934141.

Lambert, Craig. "The New Ancient Trend in Medicine: Scientific Scrutiny of 'Alternative' Therapies." *Harvard Magazine*, March–April 2002. Accessed at http://harvardmagazine.com/2002/03/the-new-ancient-trend-in.html.

Long, Katherine. "Bastyr Chapel architect sets record straight on acoustics." *The Seattle Times*, August 10, 2009. Accessed at http://seattletimes.com/html/localnews/2009630626_bastyr10m.html.

National College of Natural Medicine. "NCNM to Recognize Dr. Les Griffith for Outstanding Service: Leader in natural medicine will receive honorary degree" [press release]. National College of Natural Medicine. May 11, 2010. Accessed at http://www.naturopathic.org/Files/eNews/NCNM%20Press%20Release%20-%20Les%20Griffith,%20ND.pdf.

Perry, Nick. "Bastyr U. carves niche in alternative health care." *The Seattle Times*, December 22, 2003. Accessed at http://seattletimes.com/html/localnews/2001820727_bastyr22e.html.

Pizzorno, Joseph E., and Michael T. Murray. *Textbook of Natural Medicine*, 4th Edition. Elsevier Health Sciences, 2012.

Sisson, Paul. "Natural Medical School Latest Development in Growing Trend." *San Diego Union-Tribune*. December 9, 2012. Accessed at http://www.utsandiego.com/news/2012/dec/09/tp-natural-medical-school-latest-development-in/?#article-copy.

Whorton, James C. *Nature Cures: The History of Alternative Medicine in America*. Oxford University Press, 2004.

Editor: Kent Sturgis
Proofreader, indexer: Karen Olson
Cover & text design: Elizabeth M. Watson, Watson Graphics
Digital prepress: William Campbell, Mars Premedia
Print production: Susan Dupèrè
Publication management: Kent Sturgis Publishing Services, LLC

Library of Congress Control Number: 2015941413
ISBN 978-0-692-43031-6

Photo credits—All photos published in *Rooted in Health* were provided
courtesy of Bastyr University, except for certain images published with
permission of the following photographers and stock photo agencies: Mark
Frey, page 20 and page 68; Cartela/Shutterstock.com, page 34;
Keith Lamond/Shutterstock.com, page 46; Thinkstock.com, page 55;
Lara Swimmer, page 92 and page 93 (top).
Front cover photo—Echinacea, from the daisy family, courtesy of
Bastyr University.

First Edition
5 4 3 2 1
Printed in Canada

For more information:
Bastyr University
14500 Juanita Dr. NE
Kenmore, WA 98028
(425) 602-3000
www.bastyr.edu

INDEX

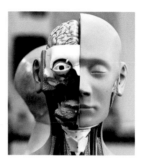

OUR VISION

*As the world's leading academic
center for advancing and integrating
knowledge in the natural health arts and
sciences, Bastyr will transform the
health and well-being of the
human community.*